OFFSHORE OIL AND GAS RESOURCES IN THE U.S., CUBA AND ISRAEL

ENERGY SCIENCE, ENGINEERING AND TECHNOLOGY

Additional books in this series can be found on Nova's website under the Series tab.

Additional E-books in this series can be found on Nova's website under the E-book tab.

ENERGY SCIENCE, ENGINEERING AND TECHNOLOGY

OFFSHORE OIL AND GAS RESOURCES IN THE U.S., CUBA AND ISRAEL

ETHAN L. CONRAD
EDITOR

Nova Science Publishers, Inc.
New York

Copyright © 2012 by Nova Science Publishers, Inc.

For permission to use material from this book please contact us:
Telephone 631-231-7269; Fax 631-231-8175
Web Site: http://www.novapublishers.com

Library of Congress Cataloging-in-Publication Data

Offshore oil and gas resources in the U.S., Cuba, and Israel / editor, Ethan L. Conrad.
       p. cm.
   Includes index.
   ISBN 978-1-62100-256-7 (softcover)
   1.   Offshore oil well drilling--United States. 2.   Offshore oil well drilling--Cuba. 3. Offshore oil well drilling--Israel. 4. Offshore gas well drilling--United States. 5. Offshore gas well drilling--Cuba. 6. Offshore gas well drilling--Israel. 7. Petroleum in submerged lands--United States. 8. Petroleum in submerged lands--Cuba. 9. Petroleum in submerged lands--Israel. I. Conrad, Ethan L.
   TN871.3.O347 2011
   333.8'230916--dc23
                                                    2011032390

Published by Nova Science Publishers, Inc. † New York

CONTENTS

PREFACE

This book explores the prospects and processes of offshore oil and gas resources in the U.S., Cuba and Israel. Access to potential oil and gas resources under the U.S. Outer Continental Shelf continues to be controversial. The oil spill that occurred on April 20th, 2010, in the Gulf of Mexico brought increased attention to offshore drilling risks. Cuba is moving toward development of its offshore oil resources. While the country has proven oil reserves of just 0.1 billion barrels, the U.S. Geological Survey estimates that offshore reserves in the North Cuba Basin could contain an additional 4.6 billion barrels of undiscovered technically recoverable crude oil. Israel has been dependent on energy imports since it became a nation in 1948, but recent offshore natural gas discoveries could change that and possibly make Israel an exporter of natural gas.

Chapter 1- Access to potential oil and gas resources under the U.S. Outer Continental Shelf (OCS) continues to be controversial. Moratoria on leasing and development in certain areas were largely eliminated in 2008 and 2009, although a few areas remain legislatively off limits to leasing. The 112th Congress may be unlikely to reinstate broad leasing moratoria, but some members have expressed interest in protecting areas (e.g., the Georges Bank or Northern California) or establishing protective coastal buffers. Pressure to expand oil and gas supplies and protect coastal environments and communities will likely lead Congress and the Administration to consider carefully which areas to keep open to leasing and which to protect from development.

Chapter 2- Cuba is moving toward development of its offshore oil resources. While the country has proven oil reserves of just 0.1 billion barrels, the U.S. Geological Survey estimates that offshore reserves in the North Cuba Basin could contain an additional 4.6 billion barrels of undiscovered technically recoverable crude oil. The Spanish oil company Repsol, in a consortium with Norway's Statoil and India's Oil and Natural Gas Corporation, is expected to begin offshore exploratory drilling in 2011, and a number of other companies are considering exploratory drilling. At present, Cuba has six offshore projects with foreign oil companies. If oil is found, some experts estimate that it would take at least three to five years before production would begin. While it is unclear whether offshore oil production could result in Cuba becoming a net oil exporter, it could reduce Cuba's current dependence on Venezuela for oil supplies.

Chapter 3- Israel has been dependent on energy imports since it became a nation in 1948, but the recent offshore natural gas discoveries could change that and possibly make Israel an exporter of natural gas. Development of the recently discovered natural gas fields—Tamar, Dalit, and Leviathan—likely will decrease Israel's needs for imported natural gas, imported coal, and possibly imported oil. A switch to natural gas would most likely affect electric generation, but could also improve Israel's trade balance and lessen carbon dioxide emissions. Regionally, Israel's success thus far has sparked interest from its neighbors to explore their boundaries for energy resources and has raised concerns from Lebanon about sovereignty over the discoveries. Development of these new resources, and possibly other discoveries, would enhance Israel's economic and energy security. Israel is in the early stages of formulating the regulatory framework to oversee the development of these resources and may seek assistance from the United States or other natural gas producing countries in weighing its options.

Key Points:

- The new discoveries—depending upon the actual production—could represent over 200 years' worth of Israel's current natural gas consumption.
- Israel's electrical generation sector will likely be the beneficiary of the new natural gas resources.
- Additional natural gas and possibly oil resources may exist.

In: Offshore Oil and Gas Resources in the U.S. ...   ISBN: 978-1-62100-256-7
Editor: Ethan L. Conrad   © 2012 Nova Science Publishers, Inc.

Chapter 1

U.S. OFFSHORE OIL AND GAS RESOURCES: PROSPECTS AND PROCESSES

Marc Humphries, Robert Pirog and Gene Whitney

SUMMARY

Access to potential oil and gas resources under the U.S. Outer Continental Shelf (OCS) continues to be controversial. Moratoria on leasing and development in certain areas were largely eliminated in 2008 and 2009, although a few areas remain legislatively off limits to leasing. The 112th Congress may be unlikely to reinstate broad leasing moratoria, but some members have expressed interest in protecting areas (e.g., the Georges Bank or Northern California) or establishing protective coastal buffers. Pressure to expand oil and gas supplies and protect coastal environments and communities will likely lead Congress and the Administration to consider carefully which areas to keep open to leasing and which to protect from development.

The oil spill that occurred on April 20, 2010, in the Gulf of Mexico brought increased attention to offshore drilling risks. Consideration of offshore development for any purpose has raised concerns over the protection of the marine and coastal environment. In addition to the oil spill, historical events associated with offshore oil production, such as the large oil spill off the coast of Santa Barbara, CA, in 1969, cause both opponents and proponents of offshore development to consider the risks and to weigh those risks against the economic and social benefits of the development.

On December 1, 2010, the Obama Administration announced its Revised Program (RP) for the remainder of the 2007-2012 OCS Leasing Program. Among other components, the RP eliminates five Alaskan lease sales (sales 209, 212, 214, 217, and 221) that had been contemplated in the current lease program. Lease sale 219 in the Cook Inlet (scheduled to be held in 2011) was cancelled because of a lack of industry interest. Further, the Obama Administration, under executive authority, withdrew the North Aleutian Basin Planning Area from oil and gas leasing activity until June 30, 2017. Public hearings began in 2010 on the scope of the 2012-2017 OCS oil and gas leasing program, but the RP excludes all three Atlantic and all four Pacific Coast planning areas at least through 2017. Three planning areas in Alaska (Cook Inlet, Chukchi, and Beaufort Sea) are being scoped as well. Since the Deepwater Horizon oil spill, President Obama has cancelled the August lease sale (215) and the Mid-Atlantic lease sale (220).

Exploration and production proceed in stages during which increasing data provide increasing certainty about volumes of oil and gas present. Prior to discovery by drilling wells, the estimated volumes of oil and gas are termed undiscovered resources. The Bureau of Ocean Energy Management, Regulation, and Enforcement (BOEMRE) conducts assessments of undiscovered technically recoverable resources (UTRR) on the U.S. OCS. The statistical certainty of these assessment estimates varies by region because the availability of geologic data varies widely by region. For example, the extensive exploration and production histories of central and western Gulf of Mexico and Southern California provide a comparatively greater amount of geologic data to use for assessments. In contrast, much of the remainder of the U.S. OCS has seen little exploration and production of oil and gas and therefore detailed geologic information is lacking.

One characteristic of the U.S. oil market, as well as of world oil markets, is that the access to supply tends to be sequential. Normally, the first source of oil used by a nation is domestic production, if available. Typically, the next source of supply is imports from countries not party to the Organization of the Petroleum Exporting Countries (OPEC). Finally, residual demand is met by OPEC. The ultimate impact of oil and gas development in offshore areas will depend on oil and gas prices, volumes of resources actually discovered, infrastructure development, and restrictions placed on development, all of which currently carry significant uncertainties.

INTRODUCTION AND BACKGROUND

In the wake of the Deepwater Horizon explosion and oil spill in the Gulf of Mexico on April 20, 2010, Congress continues to debate how much of the outer continental shelf (OCS) should be available for oil and gas development. Having all of the OCS available is seen by some as a way to increase domestic supply and improve U.S. energy security; others contend that OCS development has risks for the coastal environment and coastal communities, and that other options are available for energy security. The issue remains contentious, as industry would prefer that the entire OCS remain available without any area exclusions such as buffer zones (e.g., 25 or 50 miles from the coastline) or withdrawals. Industry might be reluctant to invest in any new resource assessments unless they are confident that the OCS will remain open for long-term leasing and development. Environmental groups have argued to retain the OCS moratoria as previously specified and that industry already has access to areas in the Gulf of Mexico with large oil and gas reserves as well as several thousand leases not yet developed.

Following the Deepwater Horizon oil spill the Obama Administration saw an immediate need to review and upgrade drilling and safety rules for offshore oil and gas development. The 2010 oil spill changed the landscape for offshore oil and gas development. It has led to the reorganization of the Minerals Management Service (MMS) (discussed below), rewriting safety rules for drilling offshore, a suspension of permitting and drilling operations for some, review of the role of the National Environmental Policy Act (NEPA) and use of categorical exclusions, and a revised leasing program (announced December 1, 2010). Many in the oil and gas industry asserted that the six-month suspension that was announced on May 28, 2010 (called a "de-facto" moratoria) caused significant disruption of development activities and will lead to a reduction of oil and gas production and other economic losses at least in the short term. However, according to the EIA reference case, crude oil production from the lower 48 offshore region is estimated to increase from 1.71 million barrels per day (mb/d) in 2009 to 1.81 mb/d in 2015.[1] New deepwater drilling permits were not issued until February 28, 2011. Ten new drilling permits have been issued as of April 8, 2011.

The Former MMS[2]

On May 11, 2010, Secretary of the Interior Ken Salazar announced a plan to separate the safety and environmental functions of the Minerals Management Service (MMS) from its leasing and revenue collection function. The goal was to improve the efficiency and effectiveness of the agency. Subsequently, on May 19, 2010, a decision was made by the Secretary to establish the following three new entities to perform the functions of the MMS: Bureau of Ocean Energy Management (BOEM), Bureau of Safety and Environmental Enforcement (BSEE), and the Office of Natural Resources Revenue (ONRR).[3] BOEM and BSEE functions currently reflect a transitional framework within the Bureau of Ocean Energy Management, Regulation, and Enforcement (BOEMRE). Each of the three new entities as proposed are to have a director who would be under the supervision of an assistant secretary.

OCS Moratorium[4]

Oil and gas development moratoria in the OCS along the Atlantic and Pacific coasts, parts of Alaska, and the Gulf of Mexico had been in place since 1982, as a result of public laws and executive orders of the President. On July 14, 2008, President Bush lifted the executive moratoria, which included planning areas along the Atlantic and Pacific coasts. On September 30, 2008, moratoria provisions in annual appropriations laws expired, allowing these areas to potentially open for oil and gas leasing activity. The eastern Gulf of Mexico and a portion of the central Gulf of Mexico, however, continue under a moratorium established by separate statute. The Gulf of Mexico Energy Security Act of 2006 (GOMESA, P.L. 109-432), placed nearly all of the eastern Gulf of Mexico under a leasing and drilling moratorium until 2022 but allowed leasing in designated portions of the eastern Gulf. Thus, most of the eastern Gulf of Mexico remains off limits to development because it was not part of the executive OCS ban that was lifted by President Bush, nor part of the annual congressional ban that was not continued.

On December 1, 2010, the Obama Administration announced its Revised Program (RP) for the remainder of the 2007-2012 OCS Leasing Program. Among other components, the RP eliminates five Alaskan lease sales (sales 209, 212, 214, 217, and 221) that had been contemplated in the current lease program. Lease sale 219 in the Cook Inlet (scheduled to be held in 2011) was cancelled because of a lack of industry interest. Further, the Obama

Administration, under executive authority, withdrew the North Aleutian Basin Planning Area from oil and gas leasing activity until June 30, 2017. Public hearings began in 2010 on the scope of the 2012-2017 OCS oil and gas leasing program, but the RP excludes all three Atlantic and all four Pacific Coast planning areas at least through 2017. Three planning areas in Alaska (Cook Inlet, Chukchi, and Beaufort Sea) are being scoped as well. Since the Deepwater Horizon oil spill, President Obama has cancelled the August lease sale (215) and the Mid-Atlantic lease sale (220).

Recent high oil and gasoline prices have led to some renewed calls by some members of Congress for increased domestic oil development, a push to include more of the OCS in the next five-year leasing program, and an assurance of already scheduled lease sales to go forward in the current five-year program. These legislation proposals are discussed below.

This report examines questions around lifting the moratoria on OCS exploration and production and the significance of the change on U.S. oil and natural gas supplies and markets. The report presents the current U.S. oil and gas supply and demand picture and provides a discussion of legislative issues, resource assessments, the leasing system, and environmental and social issues associated with offshore oil and gas development.

LEGISLATIVE ISSUES

Although reinstatement of a blanket moratorium on the OCS is unlikely in the 112th Congress, some Members of Congress have expressed interest in protecting selected areas of the OCS (e.g., Georges Bank in the North Atlantic Planning Area or Northern California) or buffer zones of 25 or 50 miles off the coast. Some have argued for open but restricted access. The President has the administrative authority to place areas of the OCS under a leasing and development moratoria,[5] whereas legislated moratoria must be signed by the President. To open the Eastern Gulf of Mexico, GOMESA would need to be amended or repealed. Congress and the Administration are likely to give careful consideration to which parts of the OCS to keep open and which to protect through leasing moratoria. The Revised Lease Program for the remainder of 2007-2012 and the Scoping for the 2012-2017 Leasing Program currently excludes the Atlantic and Pacific coasts.

There is legislation (H.R. 1230) before Congress that would require the Secretary of the Interior to conduct four lease sales (lease sales 216, 218, 220, and 222) within about a year of the bill's enactment. The Administration's

Revised Program is scheduled to hold three more lease sales (sales 216, 218, and 222) in the Central or Western Gulf of Mexico as part of the 2007-2012 Leasing Program. Another bill (H.R. 1229) would provide a new safety review and seek to expedite the drill permitting process by providing a new timeline for the Secretary to make a final decision on the permit application. The bill includes language on judicial reviews that would provide timelines, an exclusive venue for civil actions, and limits on relief and attorney fees. A third bill (H.R. 1231) would require BOEMRE to offer lease sales in the most prospective areas in each of the OCS Planning Areas for the 2012-2017 5-Year Leasing Program, specifically, areas that contain more than 2.5 billion barrels of oil or more than 7.5 trillion cubic feet of natural gas. Increased production goals would be established at 3 million barrels per day (mb/d) of oil and 10 billion cubic feet (bcf) of natural gas per day by 2027.

The Revised Program confirms plans to determine if seismic studies should be conducted. Would this additional information on the OCS prior to lease sales generate more interest in those areas and possibly generate more revenue in higher bonus bids and high royalty rates (16.7% or 18.75%) as part of the lease terms? A related controversial legislative issue is whether coastal producing states should receive a greater share of those revenues. Revenue sharing is discussed in more detail below.

Generally, proponents and opponents alike would argue that some sense of certainty is desirable. Industry proponents, for example, want to know, if the industry invests in exploration and development and finds oil and natural gas, whether it could then move forward with production. And conversely, if certain areas are placed off limits or restricted, would those limitations remain in place for the long term? The balance of this report provides information to inform this debate.

U.S. OIL AND GAS SUPPLY AND DEMAND

U.S. Oil Markets

Consumption of petroleum products in the United States has averaged more than 20 million barrels per day (mbd) over the last seven years.

Table 1 shows that almost half of petroleum consumption has been in the form of motor gasoline used in automobiles and light trucks. The data for 2008 through 2010, which show declines in both gasoline and total petroleum product consumption, reflect two economic conditions. In the second and third quarters of 2008, the price of oil increased to record-high levels, reaching over $145 per barrel in July 2008. The high price of oil caused the price of gasoline to rise to over $4 per gallon in June and July 2008. High prices reduced consumer demand. In addition, the recession and associated financial market problems that affected the U.S. economy in 2008 also contributed to the decline in petroleum product demand by reducing consumer income and wealth. The recession, which continued through 2009, resulted in negative demand growth. Uncertainty surrounding supply disruptions resulting from political turmoil in the Middle East and North Africa have again driven oil and gasoline prices up in the spring of 2011.

Table 1. U.S. Petroleum Consumption, 2004-2010 (millions of barrels per day).

	Gasoline	All Petroleum Products
2004	9.10	20.73
2005	9.16	20.80
2006	9.25	20.69
2007	9.29	20.68
2008	8.97	19.50
2009	8.98	18.77
2010	9.03	19.15

Source: Energy Information Administration, April 28, 2011, http://www.eia.doe.gov/ petroleum/ data.cfm#consumption.

Table 2. U.S. Petroleum Supply, 2005-2010 (millions of barrels per day).

	Crude Oil Production	Net Imports
2005	5.18	12.55
2006	5.10	12.39
2007	5.06	12.04
2008	4.95	11.11
2009	5.36	9.68
2010	5.51	9.44

Source: Energy Information Administration, April 28, 2011, available at http://www .eia.doe.gov/dnav/pet/pet_crd_crpdn_adc_mbblpd_a.htm and http://www.eia.doe. govzdnav/pet/pet_move_neti_a_ep00_IMN_mbblpd_a.htm.
Notes: Net imports includes both crude oil and petroleum products, net of U.S. exports.

To meet the demand for oil to fuel the U.S. economy, the oil industry draws on two primary sources: domestic production of crude oil, and imports. Other sources include natural gas condensates and refinery expansion. The data in **Table 2** show that domestic production of crude oil declined through 2008, which is likely part of a sectoral decline in crude oil production that has occurred since the mid-1970s when U.S. production peaked. Production increases in the Gulf of Mexico and in the Bakken Formation in North Dakota have increased domestic production over the last two years.

A characteristic of the U.S. oil market, as well as the world oil market, is that the access to supply tends to be sequential. Normally, the first source of oil used by a nation is domestic production, if available. Typically, the next source of U.S. supply is imports from countries that are not party to the Organization of the Petroleum Exporting Countries (OPEC). Finally, residual demand is met by OPEC.[6] This behavior implies that, if the United States were to increase domestic production of crude oil and natural gas condensates, the result is likely to be an equal decrease in imports (all else being equal).

The data in **Table 2** suggest that even the price spike of 2008 was not sufficient to cause U.S. crude oil production to increase, or even stop its decline. The reduction in consumption that resulted from high prices and declining incomes in 2008 did contribute to the decline in imports observed in 2008 and 2009, and increased domestic production contributed to further decline in imports in 2010.

Offshore production of crude oil accounted for approximately 31% of total U.S. production of crude oil in 2010, down from 35% in 2004. Offshore production, as shown in **Table 3**, is divided between production in federal and state waters.[7] Within the federal waters category, 96% of crude oil production is from the Gulf of Mexico, and 3% is from waters off the coast of California. The state offshore production is largely raised from the waters off Alaska, where 51% of the state offshore total of crude oil was produced in 2010.

Production of crude oil depends on the existence of a proved reserve base. The data in **Table 4** show that, while the total of U.S. proved reserves has varied over a narrow range, total reserves were about 8% lower in 2009 than 2004. The reserve base in the federal offshore areas declined by approximately 17% in the five-year period 2004-2009. The decline in the proved reserve base occurred during a period of high crude oil prices, suggesting that the economic incentive existed to explore and develop new reserves, but other constraints might have prevented this activity in federal OCS areas until recently.

**Table 3. U.S. Offshore Crude Oil Production, 2004-2010
(millions of barrels per day).**

	Federal Offshore	State Offshore
2004	1.528	0.356
2005	1.355	0.358
2006	1.371	0.331
2007	1.344	0.312
2008	1.218	0.280
2009	1.584	0.119
2010	1.695	0.118

Source: Energy Information Administration, available at http://www.eia.doe.gov/dnav/
pet/pet_crd_crpdn_adc_mbblpd_a.htm.

Table 4. U.S. Proved Crude Oil Reserves, 2004-2009 (billions of barrels).

	Federal Offshore	Total Reserves
2004	4.691	21.371
2005	4.483	21.757
2006	4.096	20.972
2007	3.905	21.317
2008	3.903	19.121
2009	4.129	20.682

Source: Energy Information Administration, available at http://www.eia.doe.gov/dnav/
pet/pet_crd_pres_dcu_RUSF_a.htm.

As the reserve base in any field declines, and natural pressures within the reserve deposit weaken, the result is declining output of crude oil. This decline in production from the declining reserve base can be mitigated through the use of enhanced recovery methods, but the result is higher production costs.

U.S. Natural Gas Markets

Consumption of natural gas in the United States has averaged more than 22 trillion cubic feet (tcf) over the last six years.

Of the total natural gas delivered to consumers in 2010, approximately 22% was used by residential customers, 14% was used by commercial customers, 30% was used by industrial customers, and 33% was used in electric power generation. Over the six-year period 2004-2009, residential consumption was relatively constant, with variations attributable to weather conditions and the price. Commercial consumption was also relatively constant, while industrial consumption declined by about 15% but rebounded in 2010. The use of natural gas for electric power generation increased by approximately 26% over the period 2005-2010.

The 2004-2010 consumption patterns in the United States reflect the different reactions to price variations within the various sectors. Derived demand (indirect demand) from residential, commercial, and electric power generation sources are not very price sensitive, because the primary, ultimate uses of natural gas in these sectors are considered necessities: space heating, lighting, and appliances. Industrial consumption tends to be more price sensitive because when natural gas is used as a production input, as, for example, in the fertilizer industry, the produced goods are subject to international competition, and as a result passing on cost increases to consumers is difficult.

Table 5. U.S. Natural Gas Consumption, 2004-2010 (trillion cubic feet).

	Delivered to Consumers	Total Consumption
2004	20.725	22.388
2005	20.315	22.010
2006	19.958	21.685
2007	21.249	23.097
2008	21.400	23.268
2009	20.965	22.839
2010	22.168	24.132

Source: Energy Information Administration, available at http://www.eia.doe.gov/dnav/ ng/ ng_cons_sum_dcu_nus_a.htm.

Notes: The difference between total consumption and quantities delivered to consumers is gas used in the production and distribution of natural gas.

Table 6. U.S. Natural Gas Supply, 2004-2010 (trillion cubic feet).

	Domestic Production	Imports
2004	18.59	4.26
2005	18.05	4.34
2006	18.50	4.19

	Domestic Production	Imports
2007	19.27	4.60
2008	20.16	3.98
2009	20.58	3.75
2010	21.58	3.74

Source: Energy Information Administration, available at http://www.eia.doe.gov/dnav/ ng/ ng_move_impc_s1_a.htm.

Table 7. U.S. Natural Gas Proved Reserves, 2004-2009 (trillion cubic feet).

	Offshore State	Offshore Federal	Total Reserves
2004	0.79	19.3	192.5
2005	0.77	17.8	204.4
2006	0.82	15.4	211.0
2007	0.72	14.3	237.7
2008	1.17	13.5	244.6
2009	0.99	12.6	272.5

Source: Energy Information Administration, available at http://www.eia.doe.gov/ dnav/ng/ ng_enr_dry_dcu_NUS_a.htm.

Notes: Reserves are proved, dry gas.

In 2010, the United States produced about 85% of the natural gas it consumed (see **Table 6**), with 90% of the imported volumes arriving from Canada via pipeline. Liquefied Natural Gas (LNG) accounted for about 10% of imports, or about 1.3% of total U.S. consumption. LNG imports largely come from Trinidad, although Egypt, Norway, and Yemen also exported to the United States in 2010.

U.S. production of natural gas has increased since 2005 as production from unconventional sources such as shale gas has increased. As a result of increased domestic production, and the effects of the economic recession, imports decreased in 2008 through 2010. LNG, which some had forecast to become a major source of natural gas for the U.S. economy, has remained a minor component in natural gas supply, at about 1%-2%.

U.S. proved natural gas reserves have increased over the period 2004-2009 by approximately 42% (see **Table 7**), even though the nation has relied heavily on domestic supplies for consumption over the period. This result can be attributed to the development of new, nonconventional deposits of natural gas, such as shale gas. Offshore reserves have declined by about 35% over the period.

Economic Effects: Oil Market

The oil market is global in scope. Changes in demand and/or supply that take place anywhere in the world are likely to affect virtually all consumers. The key measure of price, in many cases, has responded with high upward volatility to increases in demand. This price behavior is the result of the short-run inelasticity of demand for oil and petroleum products. In the short run, inelastic demand implies that an increase in price will have a relatively smaller effect on the quantity demanded. This conclusion starts with a price change and traces through how the change affects quantities. The reverse logic is also true: that small changes in quantity can lead to relatively larger changes in price. During the period of high oil prices from 2004 through 2008, the actual quantity of oil demanded was exceeding forecast demand due to higher-than-expected world growth rates of gross domestic product. High growth in demand reduced excess capacity to minimal levels and resulted in substantial oil price increases. The economic recession moderated world growth of gross domestic product and led to stabilized demand for petroleum, but demand is rising again as the global economy emerges from the recession.

Another factor that increased in importance over the 2004 through 2010 period was the emergence of oil contracts as financial assets through commodity market investment. The extent to which this factor has contributed to the volatility of oil prices is still being debated, but the emergence of "financial oil" has introduced the role of expectations more directly into oil prices.

Both the short-run inelasticity of demand and the increased sensitivity of the oil market to expectations are likely to play a role in determining the degree to which opening offshore areas with potential resource deposits affects the price of oil.

Analyses of the effect on oil markets of opening offshore restricted areas to exploration, and ultimately, production, is complicated by the uncertainties inherent in existing reserve estimates. Since no exploration, or assessment of reserves, has taken place using modern technology, the available estimates are likely to be speculative (see detailed discussion below). Time is also a factor. Even if exploration of the tracts began this year, it would likely be five to ten years before significant production reached the market. For these reasons, rigorous quantitative estimates on the effect on the price of oil of opening these offshore areas are not possible.

Qualitative observations are possible. If the oil markets are slack when the key decision points (leasing, exploration, production, etc.) are reached, meaning significant excess capacity exists, and oil exporting nations are restricting production, the effect on oil prices will likely be minimal. If the markets are tight, the effects could be noticeable, and contribute to lower prices. The inelasticity of demand plays a role here, as a relatively small increase in expected reserves and production could have a disproportionate effect on price.

However, a lower price of oil will generally also encourage consumption. Increased consumption of cheaper oil could lead to increased carbon emissions. As long as the increased consumption due to lower price was met through the use of new domestic supplies, energy dependence would not increase. The development of the offshore areas would be unlikely to eliminate U.S. dependence on foreign energy sources, and may not even reduce it. Other, older fields are likely to have experienced further declines in production by the time the new offshore sources go into production, meaning that it is likely that these new sources of production might only replace other lost output, thereby reducing the rate of increase of foreign dependence.

The cost of developing these resources also depends on the state of the oil market at the key decision points. Construction and development costs for petroleum investment projects have escalated sharply in recent years, reflecting the high market prices for oil. Delays and rapidly increasing costs reduced the economic viability of many projects. Although a low oil price environment might reduce the tightness in construction and development markets, reducing costs, it may also reduce the likelihood that the oil companies would find development of these resources to be economically viable.

Economic Effects: Natural Gas Market

Natural gas markets differ from the oil market in that they are not global, but regional. As shown in **Table 6**, above, virtually all U.S. natural gas consumption comes from U.S. or Canadian sources. The only link between regional natural gas markets is through LNG, but the rapidly growing market for LNG predicted earlier in this decade has failed to materialize. LNG is still largely characterized by long-term, two-party supply and purchase agreements.

In the North American market, LNG plays the role of making up marginal short-falls in the demand and supply balance. As production from domestic onshore shale gas deposits increases, the role of LNG in the U.S. market will likely be small.

In this regional market structure, the development of new, offshore U.S. supplies could have a significant impact on the domestic price of natural gas, as well as contributing to U.S. energy independence of this fuel. Although the price of natural gas has not shown the same degree of volatility as oil, the United States has been among the highest priced regions in the world. High prices have caused residential consumers to allocate a greater portion of their budgets to home heating expenses. Industrial users either lose sales to overseas competitors, or cease U.S. production when domestic natural gas prices rise too much beyond those observed in other regions of the world.

The development of offshore natural gas resources is likely to further retard the development of a growing LNG system in the United States. Terminals for the re-gasification of LNG have proven to be difficult to site and permit, and expensive to build. If domestic natural gas resources, close to existing collection and distribution systems, at least in the Gulf of Mexico, could be developed, the LNG terminals might prove to be redundant, depending on the volumes of natural gas that ultimately might be recovered. Offshore natural gas development, though commonly associated with offshore oil production, will likely be less competitive in a market environment dominated by onshore shale gas development.

Greater OCS Access and Supply

The Energy Information Administration (EIA) of the Department of Energy projects that U.S. oil production would increase from today's 5.3 million barrels per day (mbd) to 6.0 mbd by 2035 with complete OCS access.[8] Because of its significant reserves and resource potential, most of the projected increase in production would reportedly come from the OCS. The EIA projected that offshore crude oil production would increase from about 1.7 mbd to 1.9 mbd by 2035 when including complete access to the OCS. The EIA projected that production from the Atlantic and Pacific planning areas after 2014 and from the Eastern Gulf of Mexico after 2025 would add 500,000 barrels of oil per day to U.S. supply. Offshore natural gas production in the lower 48 states is expected to remain roughly stable out to 2035. The EIA estimates are uncertain as to how much of the increased natural gas production would come from the formerly restricted areas.[9]

Based on mean resource estimates by the Bureau of Ocean Energy Management, Regulation, and Enforcement (BOEMRE), a report prepared for the American Petroleum Institute by ICF International estimates an increase in OCS production from areas formerly off limits of 286,000 barrels per day in 2030.[10] When ICF assumed a much larger resource base for the OCS (and without the leasing moratoria), oil production from those areas formerly off limits were estimated to increase 900,000 barrels per day in 2030.

A National Petroleum Council (NPC) study estimated that 1 million barrels of oil and 3.8 billion cubic feet of natural gas per day could be added to U.S. oil and gas supply by 2025 from areas formerly off limits if the OCS remains open along with a cumulative investment of as much as $98 billion in exploration and development projects.[11]

Prior to lifting the OCS moratoria, the BOEMRE projected a rise in U.S. domestic production on federal lands coming primarily from deepwater offshore areas in the Gulf of Mexico. According to the BOEMRE, deepwater oil already accounts for more than 70% of offshore production and 18.5% of total U.S. crude oil production. The number of shallow water lease sales dropped from 418 in 2002 to 264 in 2008, while the number of deepwater lease sales rose from 281 to 633 during that same period. Deepwater (1,000 feet or 305 meters) lease sales spiked in 1997 at 1,110, following the Deepwater Royalty Relief Act of 1995. Further, it is notable that there has been increasing exploration activity and an increase in reported finds in the Gulf of Mexico in ultra-deep (5,000 feet or more) waters since 2003.

However, new production realized from newly opened areas would depend on many factors, such as oil and gas prices; investment in exploration, discoveries, and infrastructure; and regulatory requirements. Is the development scenario likely to change much if the OCS remains open? Development of deepwater leases is much more expensive than shallow water leases, but the reserve potential and payoff are likely to be much greater in the deeper water. The Gulf oil spill of April 2010 and the associated changes in regulation of deepwater development has slowed offshore development in the short term, but the long-term impacts on offshore oil and gas development are uncertain.

OIL AND GAS RESERVES AND RESOURCES IN THE OCS

Meaningful projections or forecasts of the impact of offshore oil and gas production from areas previously under moratorium must rely on technical estimates of the oil and gas resources in those areas. The quality of those assessments depends on the methodology used and the data available. This section provides an overview of the quality of current assessments of the unexplored offshore areas and the uncertainties associated with those estimates.

Resource Estimation and Technological Change

Estimation Techniques in the OCS

Exploration and production proceed in stages during which increasing data provide increasing certainty about volumes of oil and gas present. Prior to discovery by drilling wells, the estimated volumes of oil and gas are termed undiscovered resources. When oil and/or gas has been discovered, the volumes of oil and gas are measured within pools or fields via well penetration or other technology, and are called reserves. Measured reserves are reported to the Securities and Exchange Commission by the owners of the wells.[12] Reserves have been reported for U.S. OCS areas that have been developed, such as the central and western Gulf of Mexico and some parts of the California coast, but no reserves of oil or gas have been reported along the Atlantic OCS, because there have been no discoveries, and only modest oil reserves have been reported on the Alaska OCS (30 million barrels of oil and no gas as of 2006).

In frontier areas or in undeveloped areas around existing production where little or no geophysical exploration or drilling has occurred, volumes of undiscovered oil and gas resources may be estimated based on the geological characteristics of the area. The quality of those estimates (or assessments) depends largely on the abundance and quality of geologic data available to the geologists making the estimates. The geologic characteristics of a remote area, to the extent they are known, can be compared to the oil and gas production history in a geologically similar or analogous area. The number and size of oil and gas fields vary with geologic environment, so an appropriate geologic model must be applied to the remote area. Again, more geologic information allows a more reliable assessment of undiscovered resources, whereas less geologic information results in greater uncertainty in the estimates. Secretary of the Interior Ken Salazar instructed departmental scientists from the

BOEMRE and U.S. Geological Survey (USGS) to produce an updated estimate on conventional and renewable offshore energy resources. The report, published in early April, drew primarily from previous BOEMRE and Department of Energy studies. The report concluded that there are a number of significant gaps related to environmental and energy resource data in the OCS.[13]

Because undiscovered resources of oil and gas in new areas are estimated using historical production in known areas, and because production in known areas is based on current exploration and production technology, these estimated volumes are called "technically recoverable" and are therefore referred to as undiscovered technically recoverable resources (UTRR). UTRR are estimates of the volumes of oil or natural gas likely to be recovered using currently available technologies without considering price. UTRR changes as available technology changes, but not as prices change. If an economic analysis is conducted to determine the volumes of oil and gas that could be profitably recovered under current economic conditions, those volumes are referred to as undiscovered economically recoverable resources (UERR). Estimates of UERR vary with the price of oil or gas.

Because these numbers are estimates and have been derived using probabilistic methods, three values for UTRR are normally reported: the volume of oil or gas that is 95% likely to be present, the volume that is 5% likely to be present, and a mean value. The 95% probability is the smallest number because it has the greatest certainty, and the 5% probability is the largest volume but carries great uncertainty. Many users of these assessments rely on the mean value for volumes of oil or gas present, but it is important to examine all three values to judge the uncertainty with which the volumes of oil or gas are likely to be present.

Analysis of Estimates

The assessments of UTRR on the U.S. OCS by the BOEMRE provide estimates whose statistical certainty varies by region, because the availability of geologic data varies widely by region.[14] For example, the extensive exploration and production histories of the central and western Gulf of Mexico and Southern California provide a comparatively greater amount of geologic data to use for assessments. In contrast, much of the remainder of the U.S. OCS has seen little exploration and production of oil and gas. Therefore, estimates of UTRR along the Atlantic Coast, much of the Pacific Coast, and coastal Alaska carry significant uncertainties. BOEMRE attempts to acquire geophysical exploration data (primarily seismic data) along these coasts, and purchases data to the degree they are available and if possible within their budget, but good data are difficult to acquire and much of the existing data are old.[15] Typically, initial estimates of UTRR change, sometimes dramatically, as the quantity and quality of data improve as exploration progresses. See **Figure 1**. Furthermore, no estimate of UERR has been attempted for U.S. OCS outside the currently producing areas. Therefore, caution must be exercised when attempting to forecast future production and resulting revenues from the OCS.

OCS Resource Estimates

For offshore oil, under the Known Resources category (proved reserves, unproved reserves, and reserve appreciation), the BOEMRE estimated proved and unproved oil reserves in the OCS to be 8.55 billion barrels (3.9 Bbbl proved and 4.65 Bbbl unproved). The BOEMRE categorized 6.88 Bbbl of oil as reserve appreciation. Offshore proved (14.3 tcf) and unproved (14.96 tcf) natural gas reserves are estimated to be 29.26 tcf, plus 30.91 tcf in reserve appreciation.

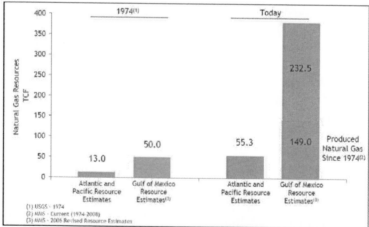

Source: Figure 1. American Petroleum Institute, 2009.

Notes: Changes in estimates for undiscovered technically recoverable resources of natural gas in the Atlantic and Pacific regions (under moratorium) and the Gulf of Mexico (developed) between 1974 and 2006. Natural gas production from the Gulf of Mexico between 1974 and 2008 is shown in green.

Figure 1. OCS Natural Gas Resource Estimates.

In the UTRR category, the BOEMRE estimated oil resources to be nearly 86 billion barrels. Of this, about 41 Bbbl oil would potentially come from the central and western Gulf of Mexico and about 25.3 Bbbl of oil would come from Alaska. With that total, roughly 66.4 billion possible barrels out of 84.24 billion possible barrels are available (about 79%) for leasing in the current BOEMRE five-year leasing program.

BOEMRE estimates the amount newly available (with the moratoria ended) at around 13.9 Bbbl.[16] For natural gas, the BOEMRE estimates a total of 420 tcf of which about 55 tcf is newly available since the lifting of the moratoria. All of the newly available areas could be included in the next BOEMRE five–year leasing program under current law. About 3.88 Bbbl of oil and 21.51 tcf in the eastern Gulf of Mexico would remain off limits.

Of the total 1.7 billion acres of the OCS, there are about 131 million acres available for leasing in the current five-year leasing program.[17] About 76% of the total acreage, but only 21% of the UTRR, was unavailable under the OCS moratoria, according to BOEMRE estimates. There are 1,600 leases in production (10.5 million acres) out of 8,124 leases (on 43 million acres) administered by the BOEMRE in the OCS.

In the near term, additional offshore reserves are likely to come from deepwater fields in the Gulf of Mexico, an area where the vast majority of leases are held and where the largest resource potential exists. Deepwater discoveries are typically much larger than those found in shallow water fields. Annual volume additions to unproved reserves, resources, and industry-announced discoveries in deepwater reached an all-time high in 2006. When it becomes apparent that a field will go into production, those unproved reserves then become proved reserves. Since 2006, there has been a 44% increase in proved deepwater discoveries in the Gulf of Mexico. But at the same time, there are vast numbers of deepwater leases going undrilled. Of the nearly 1,900 ultra-deepwater (depths of 5,000 feet or greater) leases, only 272 were drilled between 1996-2007. If the oil and gas industry continues to commit significant capital for OCS exploration and development, and deepwater discoveries are made, then the decline in offshore reserves could be slowed or reversed.

Resource Estimates by Planning Area

The BOEMRE has divided the OCS into 26 planning areas within four regions (Atlantic, Gulf of Mexico, Pacific, and Alaska). **Table 2** below lists resource assessments by Planning Area. According to the BOEMRE assessments, the areas of greatest resource potential are located in the central and western Gulf of Mexico. Taken together, these two planning areas account for about 48% of the UTRR oil and 50% of the UTRR natural gas in the OCS. Alaska accounts for about 31% of the estimated oil and natural gas potential in the OCS.

Table 8. BOEMRE Assessment of UTRR in the OCS by Planning Areas.

Planning Area	Oil (Bbbl)	Natural Gas (Tcf)
Atlantic		
North Atlantic	1.91	17.99
Mid Atlantic	1.50	15.13
South Atlantic	0.41	3.86
Total Atlantic	3.82	36.99
Gulf of Mexico		
Eastern	3.88	21.51
Central	30.32	144.77
Western	10.70	66.25
Straits of Florida	0.02	0.02
Total Gulf of Mexico	44.92	232.54
Pacific		
Washington/Oregon	0.40	2.28
Northern California	2.08	3.58
Central California	2.31	2.41
Southern California	5.74	5.74
Total Pacific	10.53	18.29
Alaska		
Beaufort Sea	8.22	27.64
Cook Inlet	1.01	1.20
Gulf of Alaska	0.63	4.65
Kodiak	0.05	1.84
North Aleutian Basin	0.75	8.62
Shumagin	0.01	0.49
St. Georges Basin	0.21	2.80
Navarin Basin	0.13	1.22
Norton Basin	0.06	3.06
Hope Basin	0.15	3.77

Planning Area	Oil (Bbbl)	Natural Gas (Tcf)
Chukchi Basin	15.38	76.77
Aleutian Arc	na	na
Bowers Basin	na	na
Aleutian Basin	na	na
St. Matthew-Hall	na	na
Total Alaska	26.61	132.06
Total U.S. OCS	**85.88**	**419.88**

Source: Statement of Stephen C. Allred, DOI/MMS, January 25, 2007

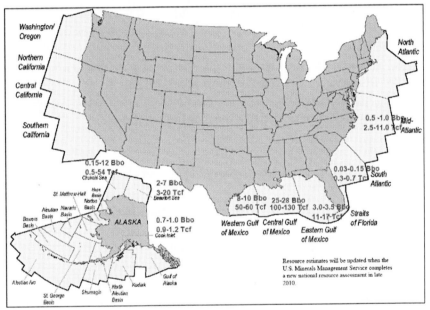

Source: BOEMRE, http://www.boemre.gov/revaldiv/PDFs/NA2006Brochure Planning AreaInsert.pdf.

Note: No price for natural gas was specified for economically recoverable natural gas resources.

Figure 2. Estimated Undiscovered, Economically Recoverable Resources (Resources at $80/bbl).

In addition, the economically recoverable resources of oil and natural gas, based on an oil price of $80 per barrel, are provided on the map in **Figure 2** for the planning areas proposed for EIS scoping under President Obama's recent directive.

Resource Estimates by Water Depth

BOEMRE Planning Areas differ considerably based on both water depth and distance from shore. (See BOEMRE website 2006 Resource Assessment Maps at http://www.mms.gov/revaldiv/ NatAssessmentMap.htm.) For example, in the North Atlantic, over half of the potential oil and gas might be located in water depths of 200 meters or less, whereas in the South Atlantic, over 70% of the oil and gas is located between 200-800 meters of water and, based on BOEMRE maps, appears to be more than 50 miles from the coast. Because of the narrow shelf off the California coast, most of the potential oil and gas resources would likely be found within 50 miles of the coast and in water depths between 0-800 meters. The eastern Gulf of Mexico is vastly different than both coasts in that the vast majority of the potential oil (84%) and gas (68%) resources are beyond 2,400 meters of water depth and beyond 100 miles from the coast. Estimates show about 15% of the potential oil and 22% of the potential natural gas might be found in less than 200 meters of water (which could also be beyond 100 miles from the coast).

THE OCS LEASING PROCESS AND PROGRAM

The Outer Continental Shelf Lands Act of 1953 (OCSLA), as amended, provides for the leasing of OCS lands in a manner that protects the environment and returns revenues to the federal government. Revenues come in three ways: bonus bids, rents, and royalties. Lease sales are conducted through a competitive, sealed, bidding process, and leases are awarded to the highest bidder. A minimum bid is determined for each tract offered. Successful bidders make an up-front cash payment, called a bonus bid, to secure a lease.

During the past 17 years, annual bonus revenues have ranged from $85 million in 1992 to $1.4 billion in 1997. Bidding on deepwater tracts in the mid-1990s led to a surge in annual bonus revenue.[18] Offshore bonus bids totaled $374 million in FY2007. But as a result of high oil and natural gas prices and the significant possible resources in the Central Gulf of Mexico, record-setting bonus bids of $3.7 billion were accepted by BOEMRE/ONRR at a lease sale in March 2008.

In addition to the cash bonus bid, a royalty rate of 12.5% or 16.7% is imposed on the value of production, depending on location factors, which can be cash or "in-kind."[19] The rate could be higher than 16.7% depending on the lease sale. For instance, lease sales 224 (March 2008) and 213 (March 2010) will require a royalty rate of 18.75% in all water depths. According to BOEMRE Congressional Affairs representatives, this higher rate (18.75%) is likely to remain in place for future lease sales. The Secretary of the Interior may reduce or eliminate the royalty established by the lease to promote increased recovery.

Annual rents are $5-$9.50 per acre (depending on water depth), with lease sizes generally ranging from 2,500-5,760 acres.[20] However, annual rental rates for the March 2009 sale in the Central Gulf of Mexico began at $11 per acre for leases in water depths over 200 meters. Bonding requirements are $50,000 per lease and as much as $3 million for an entire area.

OCSLA requires the Secretary of the Interior to submit five-year leasing programs that specify the time, location, and size of the areas to be offered. Each five-year leasing program entails a lengthy multistep process that includes an environmental impact statement. After a public comment period, a final proposed program is submitted to the President and Congress, which may be approved by the Secretary after 60 days if there is no objection by Congress.

Under current law, the primary offshore lease terms are 5, 8, or 10 years depending on water depth.[21] However, new lease terms, for blocks between 400 meters and 1,599 meters water depth, were imposed beginning with the March 2010 sale.[22] Leases continue as long as commercial quantities of hydrocarbons are being produced. If the lease is not producing oil or gas in commercial quantities by the end of its primary term, the lease reverts to the government for a possible future lease sale—unless the lessee is granted an extension. Extensions can be granted for offshore leases under 30 CFR 250.180. The regulation for offshore extensions does not specify the length of the extension nor the conditions or requirements for an extension. Also, it is not clear how often the BOEMRE grant extensions.

Many leases expire before exploration or production occurs. Data from BOEMRE on the development status for existing leases has not been made available; thus, it is difficult to classify the amount of acreage that has had no activity, is in the permitting stage, or is under exploration but not producing.

Nineteen lease sales were scheduled for the 2007-2012 leasing program.[23] Nine lease sales have occurred to date. Two lease sales were held in 2007 (sales 204 and 205), lease sale 193 in February 2008, and lease sales 206 and 224 in March 2008. Lease sale 207 was held in August 2008, lease sale 208 occurred in March 2009 and lease sale 210 in August 2009. The most recent sale (lease sale 213) took place in March 2010. The August 2011 lease sale

215 was cancelled. There are three lease sales remaining in the Revised Program.

Table 9. Lease Expirations and Relinquishments, 2001-2007.

Year	Expired	Relinquished	Total
2001	496	248	744
2002	432	224	656
2003	208	352	560
2004	155	252	407
2005	352	303	655
2006	711	280	991
2007	938	241	1,179

Source: DOI/BOEMRE.

Revenues from lease sale 224 will be shared with coastal states (Mississippi, Alabama, Texas, and Louisiana) as required by the Gulf of Mexico Energy Security Act (GOMESA). Thirteen of the 348 tracts (leases) bid on in lease sale 207 (located in sale area "181 South") also fall under the revenue sharing agreement in GOMESA (see revenue-sharing section of this report).

The Obama Administration had generally expressed support for BOEMRE efforts to facilitate development of deepwater and ultra deepwater oil and gas in the Gulf of Mexico and in the Alaskan OCS. With the moratoria lifted, leasing can occur in the newly opened areas. If the OCS remains open, it could be as much as five years or longer for lease sales to be held in the newly opened areas. Production might begin 5-10 years from the lease sale if commercial quantities are found. New infrastructure requirements (e.g., pipelines, roads, and onshore facilities) are likely to be needed, particularly along the East Coast where there has been no leasing activity in decades.

Generally, a number of concerns arise in the oil and gas leasing process that delay or prevent oil and gas development from taking place, or might account for the large number of leases held in non-producing status. There could be a lack of drilling rigs or other equipment availability, and financing and/or skilled labor shortages. Legal challenges might delay or prevent development. There are typically also many leases in the development cycle (e.g., conducting environmental reviews, permitting, or exploring) but not producing commercial quantities.

OCS REVENUES

Revenue Sharing or Not?

Federal revenues from offshore leases were estimated at $18 billion in FY2008 by BOEMRE/ONRR. During the previous 10 fiscal years (1998-2007), revenues from federal OCS leases ranged from a low of $3.2 billion in 1999 to a high of $7.6 billion in FY2006. Changing prices for oil and gas are the most significant factors in the revenue swings. Of the $18 billion offshore revenue in FY2008, $8.3 billion was from royalties and $9.5 billion came from bonus bids.

OCS leasing revenues are split among various government accounts. Revenues from the offshore leases are statutorily allocated among the coastal states, the Land and Water Conservation Fund,[24] the National Historic Preservation Fund,[25] and the U.S. Treasury. States receive 27% of all OCS receipts closest to state offshore lands under section 8(g)[26] of the OCSLA amendments of 1985 (P.L. 99-272). In FY2008, this share was over $100 million out of about $2.5 billion in total state on-shore and offshore receipts. A dispute over what was meant by a "fair and equitable" division of the 8(g) receipts was settled by the 1985 OCSLA amendments.[27]

States have argued for a greater share of the OCS revenues based on the significant impacts on infrastructure and the environment. According to the coastal producing states, the revenues are needed to mitigate environmental impacts and to maintain the necessary support structure for the offshore oil and gas industry. Revenue sharing provisions in the Gulf of Mexico Energy Security Act of 2006 (GOMESA) allow for Gulf producing states (defined as Alabama, Mississippi, Louisiana, and Texas) to receive 37.5% of revenues generated from certain leases beginning FY2007. Beginning in FY2017 and thereafter, the Gulf producing states would also receive 37.5% of the revenues generated from leases awarded within the 2002-2007 planning area, including historical leases (described in the statute). The Land and Water Conservation Fund (currently funded from OCS revenues) would receive 12.5% of the qualified revenues for state programs and the federal General Treasury would receive 50% of those revenues. BOEMRE/ONRR estimated that the states' share would total $3.1 billion through 2022 and increase to a total of $59.6 billion through 2067.

Revenues derived from lease sale 224, held in March 2008, and 13 OCS tracts in lease sale 208, held in March 2009, have been split with the four coastal states under GOMESA. Coastal Impact Assistance Program (CIAP) revenue, derived from OCS leasing revenues, is shared with coastal producing states. Based on the formula and authority in the Energy Policy Act of 2005 (Section 384, P.L. 109-58), $250 million of OCS revenues is shared annually for a four-year period ($1 billion from 2007-2010). Revenues from both GOMESA and CIAP are authorized for specific purposes (identified in the statutes) such as for the conservation, protection, and restoration of coastal areas; mitigation of damage to fisheries; and the implementation of a federally approved marine, coastal, or comprehensive conservation management plans.

For onshore public domain leases, states generally receive 50% of rents, bonuses, and royalties collected. Alaska, however, receives 90% of all revenues collected on public domain leases. There was language in the proposed draft five-year lease program (2010-2015) to encourage Congress to pass legislation that would expand revenue sharing agreements with states from future lease sales.

Royalty Revenue Estimates

The ICF International report[28] estimated that opening the OCS to production would increase federal revenues by $360 billion to $1.4 trillion (including royalties and bonuses of about $180 billion) This increase represents an increase over projected revenues (given the OCS moratoria) of 15% to 60% over the area that was classified as accessible, and assumes development of the entire economic resource base over a 30-year period.[29]

The Draft Proposed Leasing Program (DPP), 2010-2015, projected leasing revenues of $368 million based on the 30 lease sales (which includes 10 sales in areas formerly off limits) in the DPP. An additional $1.1 billion would be generated from taxes.

These estimates should be viewed with caution, as there are major uncertainties involved. First, the amount of recoverable resource is an estimate based on assumptions and probabilities; they are in fact educated guesses. Second, projecting the price of oil for a few years is difficult and complex; projecting prices for decades is highly uncertain. Lastly, possible future legislation and its terms are not known at this time, and could significantly alter revenue arrangements.

ENVIRONMENTAL CONCERNS ASSOCIATED WITH OFFSHORE EXPLORATION AND DEVELOPMENT

The environmental risks of offshore oil and gas development are being vividly displayed in the Gulf of Mexico as a result of the recent and ongoing oil spell there. In addition, historical events associated with offshore oil production, such as the large oil spill off the coast of Santa Barbara, CA, in 1969, cause both opponents and proponents of offshore development to consider the risks and to weigh those risks against the economic and social benefits of the development. Despite the use of more sophisticated drilling and monitoring tools by oil companies, the recent offshore oil spill resulting from the explosion and subsequent sinking of the Deepwater Horizon mobile drilling rig has demonstrated that catastrophic accidents may still occur, particularly associated with the more complex process of drilling in deep water.

This section describes some of the general environmental risks associated with offshore oil and gas development, and considers how those risks have changed over time. A more detailed discussion of offshore environmental issues is included in OCS Report MMS 2009-015 (see footnote 10) which describes potential impact of offshore oil and gas development on seafloor habitats, coastal habitats, marine fish resources, marine mammals, sea turtles, and marine and coastal birds.

Offshore Areas Currently Protected

In addition to limited areas in shipping lanes and military reserves, certain portions of offshore U.S. waters remain off limits to development even when moratoria are lifted. The National Marine Sanctuaries System, administered by the National Oceanic and Atmospheric Administration, was originally created under the Marine Protection, Research, and Sanctuaries Act of 1972 (MPRSA) and later amended most significantly as the National Marine Sanctuaries Act of 1992.[30] This legislation provides authority for the Secretary of Commerce, under certain conditions, to:

> designate as marine sanctuaries those areas of the oceans, coastal, and other waters, as far seaward as the outer edge of the Continental Shelf ... which he determines necessary for the purpose of preserving or

restoring such areas for their conservation, recreational, ecological, or esthetic values.

The National Marine Sanctuary System comprises of 14 sanctuaries ranging in size from less than one square mile to 137,792 square miles. Of the 14 sanctuaries, 10 are currently or potentially located within areas that might be attractive for oil and gas exploration. See box below. Oil and natural gas exploration and development are not permitted within the boundaries of the National Marine Sanctuaries, but such activities may be allowed nearby depending on specific provisions of the BOEMRE leasing programs.

Because of ongoing concerns about the effects of nearby oil and gas development on the health of the National Marine Sanctuary habitat, the BOEMRE has monitored the effects of oil and gas activities on a coral reef area of the Flower Garden Banks National Marine Sanctuary in the Gulf of Mexico for over 25 years. This effort is ongoing and conducted in partnership with the National Oceanic and Atmospheric Administration (NOAA), who administers the sanctuary. Although a buffer zone of three miles is maintained, oil and gas activities have increased in the surrounding area with no observable effects to the corals. BOEMRE requires that the nearby industry shunt wastes (dispose of through a pipe to near the seafloor) away from the banks. This mitigation was developed based on oceanographic research that indicated this would prevent these materials from coming in contact with the coral reefs.

NATIONAL MARINE SANCTUARIES LOCATED IN CONTINENTAL U.S. COASTAL WATERS[31]

Monitor National Marine Sanctuary protects the wreck of the famed Civil War ironclad USS Monitor off Cape Hatteras, NC. Established Jan. 30, 1975.

Channel Islands National Marine Sanctuary encompasses the waters surrounding San Miguel, Santa Rosa, Santa Cruz, Anacapa, and Santa Barbara Islands off the coast of California. Established Sept. 22, 1980.

Gray's Reef National Marine Sanctuary is 23 square miles just off the coast of Georgia. Established Jan. 16, 1981.

Gulf of the Farallones National Marine Sanctuary covers more than 1,200 square miles of coastal and ocean wilderness west of San Francisco. Established Jan. 16, 1981.

Cordell Bank National Marine Sanctuary gets its name from the underwater mountain that rises to within 120 feet of the ocean's surface off Point Reyes, CA, 526 square-miles. Established May 24, 1989.

Florida Keys National Marine Sanctuary is 3,700 square miles surrounding the Florida Keys. Established Nov. 16, 1990.

Flower Garden Banks National Marine Sanctuary is 50 square miles, 100 miles off the Texas-Louisiana coast. Established Jan. 17, 1992.

Monterey Bay National Marine Sanctuary is the nation's largest marine sanctuary, spanning more than 6,000 square miles of coastal waters off central California. Established Sept. 18, 1992.

Gerry E. Studds Stellwagen Bank National Marine Sanctuary sits at the mouth of Massachusetts Bay, just 25 miles from Boston. 824 square miles. Established Nov. 4, 1992.

Olympic Coast National Marine Sanctuary spans 3,310 square miles of marine waters off the Olympic Peninsula. Established July 16, 1994.

General Environmental Regulations and Requirements for Offshore Exploration and Production

All environmental aspects of offshore exploration, development, drilling, production, transportation, and decommissioning are subject to regulation. In addition to the general legal and regulatory framework that includes the OCLSA,[32] several environmental laws and executive orders have been enacted or amended since the first congressional moratorium for offshore areas in 1982, including:

- The 1990 Clean Air Act Amendments (P.L. 101-549) transferred jurisdiction over air quality from BOEMRE to EPA for all OCS areas outside the Central and Western Gulf of Mexico, and require BOEMRE to coordinate air pollution control activities with EPA. The regulations are the same as onshore leasing requirements. EPA also is setting emission limits on diesel engines and marine vessels to decrease emissions.

- The Oil Pollution Act of 1990 (P.L. 101-380), in part, revised Section 311 of the Clean Water Act to expand federal spill-response authority; increase penalties for spills; establish U.S. Coast Guard pre-positioned oil-spill response equipment sites; require vessel and facility response plans; and provide for interagency contingency plans.

- On February 11, 1994, President Clinton issued Executive Order 12898, entitled *Federal Actions to Address Environmental Justice in Minority Populations and Low-Income Populations*, which directs federal agencies, including BOEMRE, to assess whether their actions have disproportionate environmental effects on people of ethnic or racial minorities or with low incomes.

- National Fishing Enhancement Act of 1984 (P.L. 98-623), also known as the Artificial Reef Act, establishes artificial reef development standards and a national policy to encourage the development of artificial reefs that will enhance fishery resources and commercial and recreational fishing. BOEMRE adopted a national Rigs-to-Reefs policy that supports and encourages the reuse of oil and gas structures for offshore artificial reef developments, which provide valuable habitat for species of fish in areas devoid of natural hard bottom. It is anticipated that approximately 10% of OCS platforms installed would become a rigs-to-reef after decommissioning.

- President Clinton issued Executive Order 13089 on Coral Reef Protection on June 11, 1998. BOEMRE carries out the mission of E.O. 13089 by supporting coral reef research and developing mitigation measures to protect these fragile and biologically rich ecosystems.

- Other acts, such as the Shore Protection Act of 1988 (P.L. 100-688) and Marine Plastic Pollution Research and Control Act of 1987 (P.L. 100-220), require containment of trash and debris, and restrict its disposal offshore. As a result of these acts, BOEMRE has issued Notice to Lessees on awareness and elimination of marine trash and debris, which pose a threat to fish, marine mammals, sea turtles, and other marine animals.

- The 1996 amendments to the Magnuson-Stevens Fishery Conservation and Management Act (P.L. 94-265, as amended) emphasized the need to protect fisheries habitat for long-term conservation of fisheries. Under its authority, Fishery Management Plans designate essential fish habitat (EFH) for managed species. The act requires that federal agencies consult with NOAA (National

Marine Fisheries Service) about actions that could damage EFH. This process ensures consultation on fisheries of concern in a given project area.

- The National Environmental Policy Act of 1969 (NEPA, P.L. 91-190, as amended) requires that all federal agencies use a systematic, interdisciplinary approach to assess the impacts of proposed actions on the human environment; this approach is intended to ensure the integrated use of the natural and social sciences in any planning and decision-making that may have an impact upon the environment. Since its enactment, thousands of environmental assessments and environmental impact statements have evaluated the potential impacts of OCS oil and gas exploration and development on environmental and socioeconomic resources.

Environmental Impact Statements

As with many development activities, offshore oil and gas exploration and development requires environmental impact statements (EIS). The EIS provides the public with an opportunity to comment on the estimated environmental impacts of development alternatives. The OCS Report MMS 2009-015[33] summarizes the EIS process:

As required in Section 20 of the Outer Continental Shelf Lands Act (OCSLA), the MMS has established a tiered process that evaluates the potential environmental consequences for each successive management decision starting with the proposed program, then individual lease sales, and finally project-specific plans. The 5-Year Programmatic Environmental Impact Statement (EIS) analyzes the proposed leasing schedule, focusing on the size, timing, and location of proposed lease sales for the 5-year period identified in the proposed program document. The Programmatic EIS takes a broad overview of the environmental effects from the potential activities.

Once the 5-year lease sale schedule is approved, a more detailed environmental analysis is conducted for each proposed lease sale in a given area. These lease sale EISs are more detailed, including analyzing scenarios of potential activities that could result, should a lease sale occur. At this point, MMS identifies lease stipulations, which are protective of the environment, to be included in the leases granted to industry. In some cases, an EIS is prepared for multiple lease sales in a program area. This Multisale EIS is the only environmental review conducted for the first sale held in a program area. An additional environmental review, in the form of an Environmental Assessment (EA) or supplemental EIS, is conducted for each subsequent proposed lease sale to address any new relevant information. Along with the preparation of a lease sale EIS or EA, the MMS carries out informal and formal consultations with other Federal Agencies, the affected States, and the public. This includes the ESA Section 7 consultations with the National Oceanic and Atmospheric Administration (NOAA) and the U.S. Fish and Wildlife Service (FWS), an Essential Fish Habitat (EFH) consultation with NOAA, government to government consultations with tribes, and preparation of a consistency determination for each affected coastal State, as required in the CZMA.

After leases are issued, the MMS conducts environmental reviews for every exploratory and development plan to ensure that the proper environmental protective measures (mitigations) are employed. The MMS identifies site-specific mitigation measures in the form of conditions of approval. The mitigations may include avoidance of sensitive biological communities and archaeological resources, or inclusion of specialized discharge requirements.

Oil Spills and Leaks

Perhaps the greatest environmental concern associated with offshore oil production is oil spills or "blowouts." A blowout is the potentially catastrophic loss of control of the fluids in a well during drilling that releases drilling fluids, oil, and natural gas into the water, such as the Deepwater Horizon blowout and oil spill that occurred on April 20, 2010. With the drilling of oil wells and the production and transport of oil offshore, there is always some risk of oil leakage or spillage, and the serious damage that crude oil has on wildlife and on wildlife habitat is extensively documented in a number of environments. Prior to the Deepwater Horizon oil spill in the Gulf of Mexico, the industry had demonstrated some progress in reducing the risk of oil spills, as described in BOEMRE's *Draft Proposed Outer Continental Shelf (OCS) Oil and Gas Leasing Program, 2010-2015*:[34]

Since the Santa Barbara Channel OCS oil spill in 1969, measures have been underway continuously to improve the technology of offshore operations, and the Federal government has developed more stringent regulations governing OCS operations. Each OCS facility is subject to an announced inspection for compliance with environmental and safety regulations at least once a year and MMS also conducts periodic unscheduled inspections. The result of all of these efforts is an excellent record that has been documented in detail in previous 5-year program analyses and in several MMS publications. In the fifteen year period between 1993 and 2007, Federal OCS operators produced 7.49 billion barrels of oil (crude oil and condensate). During that same period, the amount of oil spilled totaled about 47,800 barrels (crude & refined petroleum spills of 1 barrel or greater) (0.0006% of that produced) or about 1 barrel of petroleum spilled for every 156,000 barrels produced.

**Table 10. Number of Spill Incidents Between 1996 and 2008
(more than 50 gallons per incident).**

Year	OCS Spill Incidents
1996	4
1997	3
1998	9
1999	5
2000	7
2001	9
2002	12
2003	12
2004	22
2005	49
2006	14
2007	4
2008	5
2009	11
2010	6

Source: U.S. Department of the Interior, Bureau of Ocean Energy, Regulation and Enforcement, *Spills - Statistics and Summaries 1996-2008*, http://www.boemre. gov/incidents/IncidentStatisticsSummaries.htm.

Notes: Data are for the oil and gas producing regions of the Gulf of Mexico and Southern California OCS. Hurricane Ivan entered the Gulf of Mexico in 2004, and most of the 2005 spills were associated with Hurricanes Katrina and Rita in the Gulf of Mexico.

Despite improvements in the offshore technologies such as improved blowout protectors and subsurface safety shutoff valves (SSSV)[35] and the accompanying reduction in the risk, equipment may fail, drilling procedures may be not be followed, and oil spills may still occur. In addition to spills that occur during general drilling operations such as the recent spill, the number of spills generally increases during hurricanes in the Gulf of Mexico, as reflected in the high number of spills in 2004 (Hurricane Ivan) and 2005 (Hurricanes Katrina and Rita). See **Table 10**. Of course, the number of spills per year does not fully communicate the impact of individual spills such as the Deepwater Horizon incident.

The BOEMRE regulations require that the producers be prepared for oil spills:

> The MMS requires that all drilling or production operations on the OCS have an approved oil spill contingency plan that describes where the nearest equipment is located, where the trained personnel are, and how everyone is notified. Additional site-specific information as to response capabilities specific to a worst case spill will be required. During drilling operations, a company can be required to have equipment staged on a dedicated vessel located at the rig, which can immediately contain and clean up a spill. There is also oil spill equipment available at onshore bases. The MMS conducts frequent inspections of all OCS activity—both at the drilling stage and at production. It also requires the use of subsurface safety valves that shut-in the flow of oil in emergencies such as loss of the entire rig or platform.[36]

Of course, the effectiveness of such measures depends upon compliance and enforcement of the regulations.

Seismic Surveys and Industrial Noise

Virtually every oil and gas exploration program involves the gathering of two-dimensional or three-dimensional reflective seismic data. Seismic data are collected by generating intense sound waves using percussive air guns towed by ships. The sound waves are propagated through seawater into the underlying sediment and rocks, and reflected sound waves are detected using an array of hydrophones towed behind the ship. These data provide images of subsurface rock strata and structures and guide exploration and development.

The impact of seismic surveys on fish and marine mammals is mixed. One study indicates that there is a local and temporary reduction in the catch of cod by fishermen after seismic data collection,[37] whereas other studies suggest little or no effect on other fish species.[38] In neither case is permanent damage to individual fish or to fish populations ascribed to seismic surveys. The effects of seismic surveys on whales and other marine mammals have been more carefully studied and have received more public attention. The rigorous study by Jochens et al. of whales and other cetaceans found no unusual effects of experimentally controlled exposure to seismic exploration on the swimming and diving behavior by sperm whales in the Gulf of Mexico.[39] A more complete discussion of environmental issues associated with offshore oil and gas exploration and development can be found in Section III of OCS Report MMS 2009-015.

APPENDIX. DEFINITION OF TERMS[40]

Proved reserves. The quantities of hydrocarbons estimated with reasonable certainty to be commercially recoverable from known accumulations under current economic conditions, operating methods, and government regulations. Current economic conditions include prices and costs prevailing at the time of the estimate. Estimates of proved reserves do not include reserves appreciation.

Reserves. The quantities of hydrocarbon resources anticipated to be recovered from known accumulations from a given date forward. All reserve estimates involve some degree of uncertainty.

Reserves appreciation. The observed incremental increase through time in the estimates of reserves (proved and unproved) of an oil and/or natural gas field as a consequence of extension, revision, improved recovery, and the additions of new reservoirs.

Resources. Concentrations in the earth's crust of naturally occurring liquid or gaseous hydrocarbons that can conceivably be discovered and recovered.

Undiscovered resources. Resources postulated, on the basis of the geologic knowledge and theory, to exist outside of known fields or accumulations.

Undiscovered technically recoverable resources (UTRR). Oil and gas that may be produced as a consequence of natural pressure, artificial lift, pressure maintenance, or other secondary recovery methods, but without any consideration of economic viability. They are primarily located outside of known fields.

Undiscovered economically recoverable resources (UERR). The portion of the undiscovered technically recoverable resources that is economically recoverable under imposed economic and technologic conditions.

Unproved reserves. Quantities of hydrocarbon resources that are assessed based on geologic and engineering information similar to that used in developing estimates of proved reserves, but technical, contractual, economic, or regulatory uncertainty precludes such reserves from being classified as proved.

End Notes

[1] Annual Energy Outlook, 2011, US. Energy Information Administration, April 2011.

[2] This report may refer to the MMS in various references or elsewhere when unavoidable.

[3] Additional information on the reassignment of MMS's responsibilities is contained in Secretarial Order No. 3299, on the DOI website at http://www.doi.gov/deepwaterhorizon/loader.cfm?csModule=security/getfile&PageID=32475.

[4] For a comprehensive review of the OCS moratorium see CRS Report R41132, *Outer Continental Shelf Moratoria on Oil and Gas Development*, by Curry L. Hagerty.

[5] OCSLA Section 12(a)

[6] This viewpoint is substantiated by Energy Information Administration data which shows that excess supply in the world tends to reside in OPEC.

[7] State jurisdiction is typically limited to three nautical miles seaward of the baseline from which the breadth of the territorial sea is measured. However, the state jurisdiction off the Gulf Coast of Florida and Texas extends nine nautical miles and for Louisiana, three imperial nautical miles. Federal jurisdiction extends, typically, 200 nautical miles seaward of the baseline from which the breadth of the territorial sea is measured.

[8] U.S. DOE/EIA, Annual Energy Outlook, 2011.

[9] Testimony of Dr. Howard Gruenspecht, Acting Administrator, EIA, U.S. Department of Energy, before the Subcommittee on Energy and Minerals, Committee on Natural Resources, U.S. House of Representatives, March 5, 2009.

[10] ICF International, *Strengthening Our Economy: The Untapped U.S. Oil and Gas Resources*, prepared for American Petroleum Institute, December 5, 2008..

[11] National Petroleum Council, *Facing the Hard Truths About Energy*, p.168, July 2007.

[12] For a full glossary and explanation of oil and gas reporting terms, see Securities and Exchange Commission: 17 CFR Parts 210, 229, and 249 [Release Nos. 33-8935; 34-58030; File No. S7-15-08] RIN 3235-AK00, Modernization of the Oil and Gas Reporting Requirements.

[13] U.S. Department of the Interior, *Survey of Available Data on OCS Resources and Identification of Data Gaps*, Report to the Secretary, OCS Report MMS 2009-015. http://www.doi.gov/ocs/report.pdf.

[14] U.S. Department of the Interior, Minerals Management Service, Fact Sheet RED-2006-01b, *Assessment of Undiscovered Technically Recoverable Oil and Gas Resources of the Nation's Outer Continental Shelf*, 2006.

[15] U.S. Department of the Interior, Minerals Management Service, OCS Report MMS 2007-049, *Geological & Geophysical Data Acquisition, Outer Continental Shelf Through 2004-2005*, 2007.

[16] Statement of C. Stephen Allred, U.S. Department of the Interior, before the Senate Committee on Energy and Natural Resources, Resource Estimate Table, January 25, 2007.

[17] The amount of acreage available in the OCS under the 2007-2012 leasing plan was listed at 181 million acres in the U.S. DOI, MMS, *Budget Justifications*, FY2010, p. 9, but the April 2, 2010 announcement to eliminate five Alaskan sales reduced the available acreage by about 50 million acres.

[18] U.S. Department of the Interior, FY2002 Budget Justifications, p. 63.

[19] A royalty-in-kind payment would be in the form of barrels of oil or cubic feet of natural gas.

[20] The annual rental rate is usually $5-$6.25 per acre in water depths less than 200 meters and $7-$9.50 per acre in water depths of 200 meters or more.

[21] The primary term is 5 years for shallow water (<400 meters deep), 8 years for leases in water 400-799 meters deep, and 10 years for deepwater leases 800 meters and beyond.

[22] Initial lease terms for blocks between 400 meters to 799meters water depth would be for five years which could be extended to eight years with a spudded well. Blocks between 800 meters to 1,599 meters water depth would receive a seven-year initial lease which could be extended to 10 years with a spudded well.

[23] Since 1983, a typical OCS lease sale would consist of thousands of leases/tracts being offered (as high as 8,800 tracts offered in a 1984 lease sale), but only as many as several hundred receiving bids.

[24] For details on the Land and Water Conservation Fund, see CRS Report RL33531, *Land and Water Conservation Fund: Overview, Funding History, and Issues*, by Carol Hardy Vincent.

[25] Under the National Historic Preservation Act (16 U.S.C. 470 et. seq.), the National Historic Preservation Fund is authorized to receive $150 million annually from OCS receipts. Authorization for this act expired at the end of FY2005, thus no funds were disbursed from OCS receipts in FY2006. After reauthorization in December 2006, funding from OCS receipts resumed in FY2007.

[26] The 8(g) revenue stream is the result of a 1978 OCSLA amendment that provides for a "fair and equitable" sharing of revenues from section 8(g) common pool lands. These lands are defined in the amendments as submerged acreage lying outside the standard three-nautical-mile state-federal demarcation line, typically extending to a total of six nautical miles offshore (or three miles beyond the state's boundary) but that include a pool of oil common to both federal and state jurisdiction. The states' share of the revenue (27%) was established by the OCSLA amendments of 1985 (P.L. 99-272) and is paid directly to the states. Payments to the states previously had been placed in escrow, which were then paid out between 1986 and 2001.

[27] U.S. Department of the Interior, Minerals Management Service, *Mineral Revenues 2000*, p. 95.

[28] *Strengthening Our Economy: The Untapped U.S. Oil and Gas Resources*, December 5, 2008.

[29] Ibid, p. 9.

[30] Listed in order of creation. For more information, see Legislative History of the National Marine Sanctuaries Act at http://sanctuaries.noaa.gov/about/legislation/leg_history.html.

[31] http://sanctuaries.noaa.gov/welcome.html

[32] For more information on the legal aspects of offshore oil and gas development, see CRS Report RL33404, *Offshore Oil and Gas Development: Legal Framework*, by Adam Vann.

[33] Op. cit.

[34] Department of the Interior, Minerals Management Service, *Draft Proposed Outer Continental Shelf (OCS) Oil and Gas Leasing Program 2010-2015*, January, 2009: http://www.mms.gov/5-year/PDFs/2010-2015/DPP%20FINAL%20(HQPrint%20with%20landscape%20maps,%20map%2010).pdf.

[35] MMS published in December of 2000 the final rule (Section 30, Code of Federal Regulations, Part 250) which included the international standard that specifies the minimum acceptable requirements for subsurface safety valve equipment. The SSSV will shut off flow of hydrocarbons in the event of an emergency and is considered the last line of defense in securing a well and/or preventing pollution.

[36] Ibid.

[37] A. Engas, et al., "Effects of seismic shooting on local abundance and catch rates of cod (Gadus morhua) and haddock (Melanogrammus aeglefinus)," *Canadian Journal of Fisheries and Aquatic Sciences*, vol. 53, no.10, 1996, pp. 2238-2249.

[38] J. Dalen and G.M. Knutsen, "Scaring effects in fish and harmful effects on eggs, larvae and fry by offshore seismic explorations." In: H.M Merklinger (ed.), *Progress in Underwater Acoustics*, Plenum Press, NY, 1986.

[39] A. D. Jochens et al., *Sperm whale seismic study in the Gulf of Mexico: Synthesis report*. U.S. Dept. of the Interior, Minerals Management Service, Gulf of Mexico OCS Region, New Orleans, LA., OCS Study MMS 2008-006, 2008, 341 pp.

[40] Definitions of terms taken from Report to the Secretary, op. cit., MMS 2009-015, Appendix A, List of Terms Used.

In: Offshore Oil and Gas Resources in the U.S. ...   ISBN: 978-1-62100-256-7
Editor: Ethan L. Conrad   © 2012 Nova Science Publishers, Inc.

Chapter 2

CUBA'S OFFSHORE OIL DEVELOPMENT: BACKGROUND AND U.S. POLICY CONSIDERATIONS

Neelesh Nerurkar and Mark P. Sullivan

SUMMARY

Cuba is moving toward development of its offshore oil resources. While the country has proven oil reserves of just 0.1 billion barrels, the U.S. Geological Survey estimates that offshore reserves in the North Cuba Basin could contain an additional 4.6 billion barrels of undiscovered technically recoverable crude oil. The Spanish oil company Repsol, in a consortium with Norway's Statoil and India's Oil and Natural Gas Corporation, is expected to begin offshore exploratory drilling in 2011, and a number of other companies are considering exploratory drilling. At present, Cuba has six offshore projects with foreign oil companies. If oil is found, some experts estimate that it would take at least three to five years before production would begin. While it is unclear whether offshore oil production could result in Cuba becoming a net oil exporter, it could reduce Cuba's current dependence on Venezuela for oil supplies.

In the aftermath of the Deepwater Horizon oil spill in the Gulf of Mexico, some Members of Congress and others have expressed concern about Cuba's development of its deepwater petroleum reserves so close to the United States. They are concerned about oil spill risks and about the status of disaster preparedness and coordination with the United States in the event of an oil spill. Dealing with these challenges is made more difficult because of the longstanding poor state of relations between Cuba and the United States. If an oil spill did occur in the waters northwest of Cuba, currents in the Florida Straits could carry the oil to U.S. waters and coastal areas in Florida, although a number of factors would determine the potential environmental impact. If significant amounts of oil did reach U.S. waters, marine and coastal resources in southern Florida could be at risk.

With regard to disaster response coordination, the United States and Cuba are not parties to a bilateral agreement on oil spills. While U.S. oil spill mitigation companies can be licensed by the Treasury and Commerce Departments to provide support and equipment in the event of an oil spill, some energy and policy analysts have called for the Administration to ease regulatory restrictions on the transfer of U.S. equipment and personnel to Cuba that would be needed to combat a spill. Some have also called for more formal U.S.-Cuban government cooperation and planning to minimize potential damage from an oil spill. Similar U.S. cooperation with Mexico could be a potential model for U.S.-Cuban cooperation, while two multilateral agreements on oil spills under the auspices of the International Maritime Organization also could provide a mechanism for some U.S.-Cuban engagement on oil pollution preparedness and response.

To date in the 112th Congress, two legislative initiatives have been introduced taking different approaches toward Cuba's offshore oil development. H.R. 372 would authorize the Secretary of Interior to deny oil leases and permits to those companies that engage in activities with the government of any foreign country subject to any U.S. government sanction or embargo. S. 405 would require companies conducting oil operations off the coast of Cuba to submit an oil response plan for their Cuba operations if they wanted to lease drilling rights in the United States. The bill would also require the Secretary of the Interior to begin efforts toward the development and implementation of oil spill response plans for nondomestic oil spills in the Gulf of Mexico, including recommendations on joint contingency plan with Mexico, Cuba, and the Bahamas.

INTRODUCTION

Long dependent on oil imports, Cuba has invited foreign companies to explore for and produce petroleum in its north offshore region, which potentially could hold almost 5 billion barrels of reserves. One of those companies, Spain-based Repsol, is expected to start exploratory drilling in 2011. A number of other companies, all government-owned national oil companies except for Repsol, are also considering exploratory offshore drilling in Cuban waters. Exploratory drilling in Cuba falls within 50 miles of the Florida coast.

Cuba's offshore development so close to the United States raises implications for U.S. policy focusing on oil spill risks and the status of U.S.-Cuban cooperation on preparedness and response in the case of a major oil spill. The Deepwater Horizon oil spill in the U.S. Gulf of Mexico heightened concerns about oil spill risks and raised the potential of U.S.-Cuban engagement regarding a potential oil spill in Cuban waters. However, the prospects for addressing these concerns are complicated by longstanding U.S. policy to isolate communist Cuba.

This report first examines Cuba's oil sector, including current production and consumption levels. It then looks at Cuba's offshore development, including the Repsol project, other offshore projects involving state-oowed foreign oil companies, and the outlook for Cuba's offshore oil production. The report then analyzes considerations for the United States raised by Cuba's offshore oil development, examining oil spill risks and environmental dangers if spilled oil reaches U.S. waters, the status of disaster coordination between the United States and Cuba, and potential approaches on the issue. The report then examines the debate over broader U.S. involvement in Cuba's offshore oil development, and touches on two outstanding boundary issues related to Cuba's offshore oil development. Finally, the report examines legislative initiatives that have been advanced to deal with Cuba's offshore oil development.

CUBA'S OIL SECTOR

Current Situation

Cuba currently has proven oil reserves of 0.1 billion barrels and natural gas reserves of 2.5 trillion cubic feet.[1] These are located on shore or near shore, and were the focus of oil exploration and production until recently. The U.S. Geological Survey estimates that the offshore North Cuba Basin could contain an additional 4.6 billion barrels of undiscovered technically recoverable crude oil resources, as well as 0.9 billion barrels of natural gas liquids and 9.8 trillion cubic feet of natural gas.[2,3] More than 70% of that oil may be in a portion of the North Cuba Basin stretching from about 70 miles west of the west end of the island for about 300 miles eastward in a narrow band known as the North Cuba Foreland Basin (see **Figure 1**). Separately, Cuban officials claimed in 2008 that Cuban offshore resources could be as much as 20 billion barrels of undiscovered crude, but in April 2011 Cuban officials lowered those estimates to five to nine billion barrels.[4]

Cuba produced 51 thousand barrels of oil a day (Kb/d) in 2010 from the onshore or shallow, near shore fields. The output is mostly heavy, sour (sulfur-rich) crude that requires advanced refining capacity to process.[5] Cuba currently accesses offshore fields located near its northern coast through horizontal drilling from onshore rigs. Canadian companies Peberco and Sherritt developed near-shore assets from onshore block 7 (see **Figure 2**), but the Cuban government terminated that lease in 2009.

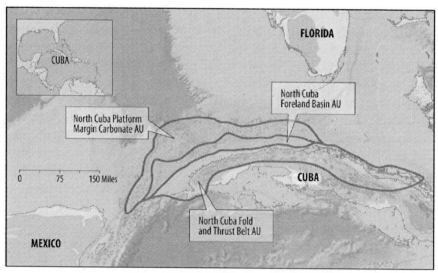

Source: U.S. Geological Survey, "Assessment of Undiscovered Oil and Gas Resources of the North Cuba Basin, 2004," (February 2005). http://walrus.wr.usgs.gov/infobank/programs/html/factsheets/pdfs/2005_3009.pdf. Adapted by CRS.
Notes: "AU" are Assessment Units.

Figure 1. North Cuba Basin (Three areas comprising the North Cuba Basin assessed by the USGS).

Cuba consumed 165 Kb/d of oil in 2009, down from 225 Kb/d two decades ago. Cuban domestic production increased and consumption fell after the Soviet Union curtailed its support for Cuba in the early 1990s. Most of Cuba's oil today is used for power generation, with relatively small amounts used for transportation. This implies net imports of 114 Kb/d. This comes from Venezuela, which has stepped into the former Soviet Union's role as a patron of the Cuban government. According to the official agreement between the two nations, Venezuela provides Cuba with oil at indexed prices and with long-term financing for up to 40% of oil imports at subsidized interest rates.[6] Cuba compensates Venezuela at least in part through offering medical and education services, including sending doctors to Venezuela.

According to the U.S. Energy Information Administration, Cuba currently has about 300 Kb/d of simple crude refining capability. However, not all of this is currently producing and Cuba has a limited amount of additional complex capacity to process the heavy sour crudes it produces. A significant amount of the oil going into power generation is burned directly as crude instead of as refined products, which can damage power plants. Of Cuba's imports, roughly 60% are refined products, mostly distillate and residual fuel oil. The rest is crude oil.[7]

Petroleos de Venezuela S.A. (PdVSA), Venezuela's state-owned national oil company (NOC), is helping *Unión Cuba Petróleo* (Cupet), Cuba's NOC, to expand and upgrade Cuba's refining capacity. Their Cuvenpetrol joint venture brought online the previously defunct Cienfuegos refinery in 2007, and they are pursing further expansion there with the assistance of the China National Petroleum Corporation (CNPC) and Chinese lenders.[8] Renovations at the Hermanos Diaz refinery and construction of a new refinery at the port of Matanzas are also planned. The upgrades may help Cuba process more of its own heavy crudes, which could be especially useful if production increases, as well as for processing crude imported from Venezuela.

Offshore Development

The Repsol Project

Repsol YPF, a publicly traded oil company based in Spain, will begin drilling an offshore exploratory well in Cuba's exclusive economic zone (EEZ) in 2011. The project, called the Jagüey prospect, is within 50 miles south of Key West, FL, according to Repsol officials. This is not Repsol's first offshore exploration venture in Cuba. It drilled Cuba's only prior deepwater well, Yamagua-1, in 2004 in offshore block 27, roughly 20 miles northeast of

Havana.[9] Repsol discovered petroleum resources, but deemed them commercially insufficient to justify producing.[10]

In its current project, Repsol leads a consortium which also includes Norway's NOC, Statoil, and India's NOC, the Oil and Natural Gas Corporation (ONGC).[11] Repsol has a 40% stake in the venture, with the other two partners each holding a 30% stake. The consortium has rights to six exploration blocks located off Cuba's northern shore (see **Figure 2**).

Repsol has collected seismic data and now awaits arrival of offshore oil rig Scarabeo-9, which it has contracted to carry out exploratory drilling from its owner, Italian oil services provider, Saipem.[12] Scarabeo-9 was built at a shipyard in Yantai, Shandong province, China. According to reports, the only major U.S. made component in the rig is the blowout preventer, equipment which failed during the Deepwater Horizon oil spill.[13] The rig has moved to Singapore, where its marine and drilling systems will be completed.[14] Sacrabeo-9 will then travel to Cuba, where it is expected to arrive and begin operations sometime in 2011. Originally expected to be completed in 2009, Scarabeo-9 has been delayed several times. According to reports, the most recent delay pushed completion from late June or early July back to August after problems encountered in transit to Singapore.[15] The rig is now expected to arrive in Cuba in September or October.[16]

Repsol has committed to Cuban authorities to drill one exploratory well, and may add additional wells depending on its results.[17] Scarabeo-9 may drill additional wells for other companies with Cuban offshore exploration and production licenses, and Malaysia's NOC Petronas is reportedly next in line, according to Repsol officials. According to Cuban officials, there are plans for five wells to be drilled between 2011 and 2013.[18]

Other Offshore Projects

Other foreign companies have five other lease agreements for offshore blocks in Cuba, and at least one more is being negotiated. Lease holders are conducting seismic surveys, and may be preparing for exploratory drilling. Apart from Repsol, the companies are all state-owned. Some of the NOCs' governments, including Brazil, Russia, and China, have recently made loans to Cuba to support development of infrastructure as well as energy, minerals, and agriculture sectors.[19]

Separate from its consortium with Repsol, ONGC contracted for two additional blocks in 2006 (see **Figure 2**). It may be preparing to move from seismic analysis to exploratory drilling as it has already started soliciting bids for necessary equipment.[20] Malaysia's NOC, Petronas, has partnered with Russian NOC Gazprom, in a contract on four blocks off the western coast of Cuba. (Gazprom and Petronas have also partnered to develop the Badra field in Iraq.[21]) They are studying seismic data and could begin drilling as early as 2011.[22] Vietnam's NOC, PetroVietnam, holds contracts for four offshore blocks west of Cuba.[23] PetroVietnam may partner with Russian NOC Zarubezhneft, which has separate contracts for onshore and near shore blocks. Venezuela's NOC, PdVSA, has a license to explore four western offshore blocks. Finally, Angola's NOC, Sonangol, signed an agreement to operate two offshore blocks in December 2010.[24]

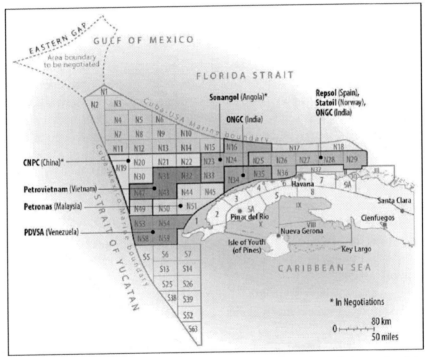

Source: Adapted by CRS from Jorge R. Piñon, Presentation given at the Inter-American Dialogue, Washington DC, October 8, 2010.

Notes: Petronas took on Gazprom as a partner in its Cuba offshore project in November 2010. Sonangol signed leases in December 2010 to operate blocks N23 and N33, while block N16 and N24 reportedly are still in negotiations. Petrobras (Brazil) signed an agreement for exploration of block N37 in October 2008, but announced its withdrawal in March 2011.

Figure 2. Cuba's Offshore Blocks.

Chinese NOC, CNPC, has been in negotiations for Cuban offshore blocks. Chinese companies have never previously drilled off Cuba's coast, though CNPC does operate some onshore production in Cuba. (Even Scarabeo-9, though it was built in China, is neither owned nor leased by a Chinese company.) As mentioned above, CNPC is also helping Cuba refurbish its Cienfuegos refinery.

Petrobras, Brazil's NOC, had signed an agreement in 2008 for offshore block N37, off Cuba's northern coast. [25] Based on seismic data it collected as well as other company priorities, Petrobras decided to relinquish its contract in March 2011. Company statements indicated that it would rather focus on oil prospects in Brazil.[26]

Outlook for Cuba's Offshore Production

Without additional information on Cuban resources, it is speculative to judge how much could be produced and when output growth would occur. Exploratory drilling from Repsol and others could provide more information on the potential for Cuban output. If oil is found, some experts estimate that companies would have to invest in developing production capacity for at least three to five years before production could begin.[27] However, production could be delayed due to a number of factors, such as the availability of offshore oil field development services. Development will take place at a slower rate than might otherwise be the case due to U.S. sanctions, which prohibit involvement from U.S. companies and prohibit use of equipment with more than 10% U.S. content.[28] Once production starts, it will likely grow slowly over the course of years. For the foreseeable future, any incremental increase in Cuban production is likely to be small relative the roughly 85 million barrel a day global oil market.

Some analysts have argued that Cuba could produce enough oil to become an oil exporter; however, this remains very speculative at this juncture. First, it is unclear how much oil is available or how quickly it can be produced. Second, Cuba would need to offset the roughly 130 Kb/d of oil it currently imports before becoming a net exporter. Third, current Cuban oil consumption may grow, especially if the economy grows or the government loosens control over oil use as more domestic production becomes available.

Cuba is still likely to trade more oil—especially as refining capacity increases—but its net trade balance for oil may not necessarily shift to a significant oil export surplus. It depends on how much oil is found and developed and what happens to domestic Cuban demand. What is more certain is that lower net import needs may reduce Cuba's dependence on imports from Venezuela.

IMPLICATIONS AND CONSIDERATIONS FOR U.S. POLICY

Oil Spill Risks[29]

The Deepwater Horizon oil spill in the U.S. Gulf of Mexico heightened concerns over the potential of an oil spill in Cuban waters and the risk such a spill could affect Florida's waters and coastal areas.[30] Current plans for drilling in Cuba fall within 50 miles of the Florida coast. Were an oil spill to occur in these areas, it could have environmental impacts in the United States. Oil can be spilled from acute exploration and production accidents, through longer-term discharge from operations, or through transportation accidents, such as a tanker collision or pipeline rupture.

Risks of a Spill in Cuban Waters

In U.S. waters, oil extraction operations are primarily governed by regulations, implemented and enforced by the Department of the Interior's Bureau of Oceans Energy Management, Regulation, and Enforcement (BOEMRE).[31] In addition, several statutes, including the Clean Water Act and the Oil Pollution Act, establish a liability regime for oil spills. Offshore exploration and production operations in non-U.S. waters may not be governed by analogous regulations or fall under a liability structure that creates an incentive to minimize oil spills. Since the Repsol project is only the second deepwater well to be drilled in Cuba's EEZ,[32] Cuban officials may still be developing regulations to prevent offshore drilling accidents and contingency plans to address accidents if they do occur.[33] However, as the recent U.S. experience in the Gulf of Mexico illustrates, even the long-time existence of regulations and regulator may not always prevent an oil spill.

According to a 2008 American Petroleum Institute study of U.S. offshore oil spills, the largest cause of spilled oil is loss of well control or "blowouts" at offshore platforms.[34] Currently, only exploration wells are planned in Cuba. Their results will be analyzed before production wells and transportation infrastructure is considered. However, there have been major oil spills from exploratory wells in the past. Two of the largest accidental oil spills in world history resulted from blowouts at exploratory wells in the Gulf of Mexico –

the Deepwater Horizon oil spill in the U.S. Gulf of Mexico and the 1979 Ixtoc oil spill in Mexico's section of the Gulf of Mexico.

It is difficult to assess the likelihood of a spill. According to Saipem, Scarabeo-9 is built to Norwegian standards, including extra equipment to shut off blown-out wells beyond what is required in the United States.[35] Repsol has significant offshore experience, including projects in the U.S. Gulf of Mexico. It has had issues with oil spills, which is not abnormal for an oil company.[36] Among other Cuban lease holders, Statoil has extensive offshore experience, including projects in the U.S. Gulf of Mexico, and are generally seen as accomplished offshore operators. Petronas, ONGC, and PetroVietnam also have offshore experience. PdVSA does not, but its offshore project appears the furthest from seeing drilling activity among existing licenses. Cuban officials claim they are taking necessary regulatory precautions, including incorporating safety practices from the United Kingdom and the United States.[37]

Risks that Oil Spilled in Cuban Waters Reaches the United States

If an oil spill were to occur in the waters northwest of Cuba, currents in the Florida Straits could carry that oil to U.S. waters and coastal areas in southern and south eastern Florida.[38] However, any environmental impact to Florida would depend on many factors at the time of a spill, including size and location of the oil spill, ocean conditions in the area, prevailing wind direction and velocity, temperature of the water and the air, the type of oil spilled, and effectiveness of any cleanup efforts. The wide variety of factors render impossible a precise description of the environmental impact were an oil spill to occur in Cuban waters.

Even if prevailing winds and current conditions favored rapid transport of spilled oil to the Florida coastline, other factors would also affect the rate of spill dispersal and, in part, determine how much of the spill reached the U.S. coast. The physical and chemical characteristics of an oil spill change over time, a process known as "weathering." How much weathering takes place after a spill occurs would affect the nature of the oil and the degree of impact. How fast oil spreads depends on volume spilled and the viscosity of the oil.[39] As the spill spreads out, the lighter and more volatile components of the oil would evaporate at a rate that depends on water and air temperature, as well as wind speed and wave action.[40] Over time, and depending on waves and turbulence at the sea surface, the spill would start to break up, or disperse. Other factors, such as oxidation, biodegradation, interaction with sediments, all contribute to the changing character of an oil spill over time and during its transport by ocean currents and winds.[41]

Finally, the extent of any cleanup activities will influence how much of the spill persists in the environment. In general, the faster and more expansive the cleanup effort, the more likely it may limit damage to the environment. (See "Disaster Coordination" below for a discussion of policy related to preparedness and response in the event of an oil spill.)

Assets at Risk If Spilled Oil Reaches U.S. Waters

If significant quantities of oil did reach U.S. waters, risks to the marine and coastal resources of Southern Florida could be of particular concern. The coastal and ocean resources of the region provide recreational, commercial, and ecological benefits to both local communities and the nation.

One of the more vulnerable areas that could be at risk is the Florida Keys and adjacent areas. The Florida Keys National Marine Sanctuary includes state and national parks, wildlife refuges, ecological reserves, research areas, and sanctuary preservation areas. North of the Florida Keys are the Everglades and Biscayne National Parks. As one moves up Florida's east coast, barrier beaches backed by lagoons and wetlands dominate the geography. And then there are the densely populated areas of Miami-Dade, Broward, and Palm Beach Counties.

The Florida Keys and adjacent areas comprise diverse and interrelated marine systems. The Florida reef is the most extensive living coral reef in North American waters, stretching for 325 miles. Reefs, sea grass beds and mangroves in the region provide habitats for many marine animals, including a number of threatened and endangered species. These coral reefs and related coastal ecosystems are valuable because they provide protection from erosion and flooding, especially from severe storms such as hurricanes.

Depending on timing, size, and location, an oil spill can cause significant harm to individual organisms and entire populations in marine and coastal habitats.[42] Spills can cause impacts over a range of time scales, from days to years, or even decades for certain spills. Acute exposure to an oil spill can kill organisms or have non-lethal but debilitating affects on organism development, feeding, reproduction, or disease immunity. Ecosystems in which they exist can also be harmed.[43] Certain habitats in the area—such as coral reefs, mangrove swamps, and salt marshes—are especially vulnerable.[44] Long-term, chronic exposure, as occurs from continuous oil releases such as leaking pipelines, offshore production discharges, and non-point sources (e.g., urban runoff) can see impacts spread from sea life to the survival and reproductive success of marine birds and mammals.[45]

Southern Florida's natural resources are closely integrated with its economic interests. Southern Florida supports significant tourism as well as commercial and recreational fishing. Florida's tourism industry directly employs more than a million people. The 84 million tourists that visited Florida in 2008 spent around $65 billion.[46] The Deepwater Horizon spill illustrated that an oil spill can significantly harm the tourism industry of affected areas. A well-publicized oil spill can even weaken tourism in a nearby area, regardless of the actual threat to human health created by the spill.

Disaster Coordination between the United States and Cuba

In light of oil spill concerns, there has been increased public interest on the status of coordination between Cuba and the United States. Coast Guard officials reportedly are reviewing U.S. contingency plans in the event of an oil spill in Cuban waters,[47] and a number of analysts and policy groups are encouraging U.S.-Cuban engagement on the issue.[48]

Currently the United States and Cuba are not parties to a bilateral agreement on oil spills. In the aftermath of the Deepwater Horizon spill, however, U.S. officials in Havana kept the Cuban government informed about the oil spill in working-level discussions. With Cuba's interest in developing its offshore oil resources so close to the United States, some analysts have called for more institutionalized or formal U.S.-Cuban cooperation and planning to minimize potential damage from an oil spill. Given the comprehensive U.S. economic sanctions on Cuba, some analysts have called for the Administration to amend or rescind regulations that restrict the transfer of equipment, technology, and personnel that would be needed to combat an oil spill in Cuba.[49] Some energy analysts assert that foreign oil companies operating in Cuba need to have full access to technology and personnel in order to prevent or manage a spill.[50] Some maintain that U.S. embargo has forced drillers to use second-hand equipment to avoid buying from U.S. companies.[51]

U.S. oil spill mitigation service companies can be licensed through the Treasury Department's Office of Foreign Assets Control (OFAC) and the Department of Commerce's Bureau of Industry and Security (BIS) to provide oil spill prevention and containment support to companies operating in Cuba. At least two U.S. companies so far have received such licenses. According to the Department of State, the United States expects any foreign oil company engaged in oil exploration activities in Cuba to have adequate safeguards in place to prevent oil spills and contingency plans to address a spill should it happen.[52]

Since 2001, a Florida-based company, Clean Caribbean & Americas, has received U.S. licenses to send technical advises and trainers to assist foreign oil companies in Cuba to prepare to respond to a large oil spill. The actual material and equipment is stored in Fort Lauderdale and would be sent to Cuba by air and sea in the event of a major oil spill.[53] For a Tier 1 oil spill, one that is small and localized, foreign oil companies drilling offshore in Cuba would maintain their own capabilities and equipment. For a Tier 2 oil spill, involving larger quantities of oil that could spread beyond the immediate vicinity where the spill took place, near shore oil operators and the Cuban government would supply equipment to help respond to the spill. A much larger Tier 3 oil spill, like a major tanker accident or an offshore well blowout, would require international assistance, like that provided by Clean Caribbean & Americas, which would move equipment into Cuba.[54] This type of oil spill response mechanism for large Tier 3 spills is a typical arrangement that has developed internationally over the past 30 years. CCA's President Paul Schuler maintains that involvement of Cuban and U.S. agencies in drills and exercises would enhance preparedness and response to a potential oil spill in Cuba.[55]

In late May 2010, OFAC also approved a license for the Texas-based International Association of Drilling Contractors (IADC) to travel to Cuba to discuss safety and mitigation of environmental hazards with Cuban authorities. After the meeting in August 2010, IADC President Lee Hunt maintained that the Cubans are eager to work with U.S. industry to ensure safer drilling.[56] OFAC also reportedly approved a license for IADC to allow Cuban officials to participate in a May 2011 conference in Trinidad and Tobago that it was sponsoring on the topic of improving industry oil industry environmental practices. A panel was specifically planned on Cuba's offshore drilling at the May 12-13, 2011 conference.[57]

U.S.-Mexico Cooperation as a Potential Model

U.S. cooperation with the Mexican government on oil spills could serve as a potential model for U.S.-Cuban government engagement on disaster preparedness and coordination. The United States and Mexico negotiated a cooperation agreement in 1980 regarding pollution caused by oil and other hazardous substances. The agreement called for the two countries to establish a joint contingency plan in order to ensure an adequate response to spills.[58]

The joint plan that was developed – known as Mexus Plan – sets forth standard operating procedures in case of pollution incidents that threaten the coastal waters or marine environment of the border zone of both countries. The plan lays out the organization of the response teams for each country, including the federal and state agencies involved. It provides for joint response teams to be formed and activated when needed, and provides for coordination, planning, and logistics of the joint response. The U.S. response team is coordinated by the Coast Guard's Assistant Commandant for Marine Safety and Environmental Protection.[59]

Following the model of U.S.-Mexican cooperation on oil spills could ensure optimal bilateral engagement with Cuba on oil spill contingency planning. Such a model would likely first entail the negotiation of a cooperation agreement on oil spills followed by the development of a joint contingency plan. Even before an agreement and plan are in place, initial discussions and dialogue on the issue could increase preparedness in the case of a spill. Once the agreement and joint plan are in place, regular meetings and periodic exercises could provide for the maintenance of the joint contingency plan.

As with U.S.-Mexican cooperation, the Coast Guard would likely play a leading coordinating role. Such Coast Guard cooperation with Cuba on oil spill preparedness and response would likely be made easier because of the Coast Guard's existing cooperation with Cuba on migration and drug trafficking issues.[60]

The final report of the National Commission on the BP Deepwater Horizon Oil Spill and Offshore Drilling, issued in January 2011, maintained that since Mexico already drills in the Gulf of Mexico and Cuba has expressed an interest in deepwater drilling in the Gulf of Mexico, that it is in the U.S. national interest to negotiate with these countries to agree on a common, rigorous set of standards, a system of regulatory oversight, and operator adherence to an effective safety culture, along with protocols to cooperate on containment and response strategies in case of a spill.[61] Mexican officials have also called for discussions between the three countries.[62]

Some energy analysts have also argued that the Bahamas should also be included in any movement in cooperation on oil spill response preparedness between Cuba and the United States since that country also is looking to eventually develop its deepwater oil and natural gas potential and because of the close location of many Bahamian islands to Cuba and the United States.[63]

As noted below, legislation has been introduced in the 112th Congress, S. 405 (Nelson), that, among its provisions, would require the Secretary of the

Interior to work toward the development and implementation of oil spill response plans for spills in the eastern Gulf of Mexico. This would require recommendations on a joint contingency plan with Mexico, Cuba, and the Bahamas.

Cooperation through Multilateral Agreements

Both Cuba and the United States are signatories to multilateral agreements that commit the two parties to prepare for and cooperate on potential oil spills. This includes the International Convention on Oil Pollution Preparedness, Response, and Cooperation (OPRC), which was adopted under the auspices of the International Maritime Organization (IMO) in 1990 and entered into force in 1995. The convention was adopted in response to a U.S. environmental initiative in the aftermath of the 1989 Exxon Valdez oil spill. Under the convention, parties are required to establish measures for dealing with pollution incidents, either nationally or in co-operation with other countries.[64] The IMO is given a central role under the convention in providing information services, education and training, and technical services and assistance.

Both Cuba and the United States are also parties to the Convention for the Protection and Development of the Marine Environment of the Wider Caribbean Region, known as the Cartagena Convention, which was adopted in 1983 and entered into force in 1986. The agreement includes a Protocol Concerning Co-operation in Combating Oil Spills in the Wider Caribbean Region. The protocol calls for an exchange of information among the signatories regarding contacts, laws, regulations, institutions, and operational procedures relating to the prevention of oil spill incidents and to the means of reducing and combating the harmful effects of oil spills. It also states that parties to the agreement should conclude appropriate bilateral or multilateral subregional arrangements as necessary to facilitate implementation. It obligates each party to assist other parties in response to an oil spill incident according to these arrangements.[65]

Short of direct U.S.-Cuban bilateral engagement on oil spill preparedness and coordination, these two multilateral agreements could provide a mechanism for some U.S.-Cuban cooperation on oil spills. For example, in order to implement the Cartagena Agreement's protocol on oil spill cooperation in the Caribbean, the IMO maintains a regional activity center in Curaçao, Netherlands Antilles, known as the Regional Marine Pollution Emergency Information and Training Center for the Wider Caribbean (RAC/REMPEITC-Caribe). The Center's objective is to strengthen the operational effectiveness of the Cartagena Agreement and OPRC through the provision of technical services, training activities, information sharing, and exercises.[66] The United States and Cuba could work through the IMO and its regional center in Curacao to engage on oil spill preparedness and coordination.

As noted above, the IMO sent a technical mission to Cuba in June 2010 to evaluate the Cuba's preparedness to respond to the Deepwater Horizon oil spill. The mission made several recommendations for Cuba to improve its national contingency plan to respond to oil spills, including the development of a training plan and increased cooperation with the IMO's regional training center in Curaçao (such as attending meeting, participating in projects, and receiving IMO assistance through this regional institution).[67]

Debate over U.S. Investment in Cuba's Energy Sector

Since the United States imposed comprehensive economic sanctions on Cuba in the early 1960s, most financial transactions with Cuba have been prohibited, including U.S. investment in Cuba's offshore energy sector. The Cuban Assets Control Regulations (CACR, found at 31 CFR 515), first issued by the Treasury Department in 1963, lay out a comprehensive set of economic sanctions against Cuba, including a prohibition on most financial transactions. The CACR have been amended many times over the years to reflect changes in policy and remain in force today. The Cuban Liberty and Democratic Solidarity Act of 1996 (P.L. 104-114), enacted in the aftermath of Cuba's shooting down of two U.S. civilian planes in February 1996, codified the Cuban embargo, including all the restrictions under the CACR. The codification is especially significant because of its long-lasting effect on U.S. policy toward Cuba. The executive branch is prohibited from lifting the economic embargo until certain democratic conditions are met. The CACR still provides the executive branch with the ability to modify the embargo restrictions, but the President cannot suspend or completely terminate the Cuban embargo regulations without first determining that a transition government or democratically-elected government is in power in Cuba.[68]

Some U.S. business and policy groups have called on Congress and the Administration to allow U.S. oil companies to become involved in Cuba's offshore oil development. Several legislative initiatives were introduced in the 111th Congress (S. 774, H.R. 1918, and S. 1517) that would have specifically authorized such activities and amended U.S. law to allow for travel for such activities (see "Legislative Initiatives" below). A major business argument in favor of U.S. involvement in Cuba's offshore energy sector is that U.S. failure to enter into the Cuban market completely hands over potential investment opportunities to foreign competitors.[69] As mentioned above, national oil companies from Russia, China, Venezuela, and elsewhere have been investing in Cuba's energy industry. In a 2009 report, the Brookings Institution offered several additional reasons for U.S. involvement in Cuba's offshore development. The report maintains: that it would help reduce Cuba's dependence on Venezuela for its oil imports; that it would increase U.S. influence in Cuba if U.S. companies had a significant presence in the county; that U.S. companies have the expertise to develop Cuba's offshore oil and gas in a safe and responsible manner; and that it is preferable to have U.S. companies involved because they have higher standards of transparency than some foreign oil companies.[70]

On the opposite side of the policy debate, a number of policy groups and Members of Congress oppose engagement with Cuba, including U.S. investment in Cuba's offshore energy development. A legislative initiative introduced in the 111th Congress, H.R. 5620, would go further and impose visa restrictions and economic sanctions on foreign companies and its executives who help facilitate the development of Cuba's petroleum resources. The bill asserts that offshore drilling by or under the authorization of the Cuban government poses a "serious economic and environmental threat to the United States" because of the damage that an oil spill could cause. Opponents of U.S. support for Cuba's offshore oil development also argue that such involvement would provide an economic lifeline to the Cuban government and thus prolong the continuation of the communist regime. They maintain that if Cuba reaped substantial economic benefits from offshore oil development, it could reduce societal pressure on Cuba to enact market-oriented economic reforms. Some who oppose U.S. involvement in Cuba's energy development contend that while Cuba might have substantial amounts of oil offshore, it will take years to develop. They maintain that the Cuban government is using the enticement of potential oil profits to break down the U.S. economic embargo on Cuba.[71]

Boundary Issues

There are two boundary issues related to Cuba's development of its offshore hydrocarbon resources. The first involves a 1977 bilateral agreement that delineated a maritime boundary between Cuba and the United States in the Straits of Florida and eastern Gulf of Mexico. The second involves an undelineated section of the Gulf of Mexico known as the eastern gap with claims by the United States, Mexico, and Cuba. (See **Figure 2**, which shows both the maritime boundary between the United States and Cuba and the eastern gap area.)

When the United States and Cuba negotiated the 1977 maritime boundary agreement, U.S. policymakers viewed it as important to avoid maritime enforcement problems and to establish an agreed limit for fisheries and continental shelf activities (such as exploitation of hydrocarbon resources). Both countries, which have opposing coasts ranging from between 77 and 90 miles apart, agreed to the provisional application of the agreement pending permanent entry into force following the exchange of instruments of ratification. While the boundary agreement was submitted to the U.S. Senate in January 1979 for its advice and consent to ratification, and the Senate Foreign Relations Committee subsequently reported the treaty favorably in August 1980, the Senate has not ratified it. According to the Department of State, final action has been deferred because of the political relations between Cuba and the United States, not because of any stated objection to the boundary.[72] Nevertheless, Cuba and the United States have exchanged diplomatic notes every two years extending the provisional application of the agreement for a two-year period. The most recent exchange of notes occurred May 20, 2010, with an effective date of January 5, 2010. As noted in State Department testimony to the Senate Foreign Relations Committee in June 1980, the provisional application of the agreement falls under the President's authority to establish boundaries, pending the full Senate's consideration of the treaty.[73] The treaty itself, in Article V, included a provision stating the parties agreed to apply the terms of the agreement provisionally, and according to the Department of State, this "constituted an executive agreement within the body of the treaty."[74]

Some Members of Congress have called on the Administration to rescind the provisional application of the 1977 boundary agreement with the view that it would likely curtail Cuba's offshore oil development. U.S. withdrawal from the agreement, however, would have no practical effect on Cuba's offshore oil development. According to then-National Security Adviser James Jones in late September 2010, withdrawal from the agreement would have no discernable effect on the Cuban government and could create further boundary claim disputes for the United States.[75]

The eastern gap – an undelineated area of the Gulf of Mexico beyond the 200-mile exclusive economic zones of Cuba, Mexico, and the United States – could potentially hold large amounts of oil, although to date there is little hard data to confirm this. The demarcation of the area is open for negotiations among the three countries, but will likely await an improvement in relations between Cuba and the United States.[76] A potential model for these negotiations is a treaty signed in 2000 between the United States and Mexico for a western gap in the Gulf of Mexico.[77] Negotiations involving three countries, however, would likely be more complicated than a single bilateral agreement with Mexico. In May 2009, Cuba made a submission to the U.N. Commission on the Limits of the Continental Shelf (CLCS) regarding the eastern gap, but all three states – Cuba, Mexico, and the United States – maintained that the submission did not prejudice the final delimitation of the outer continental shelf agreed to by these states.[78]

LEGISLATIVE INITIATIVES

Legislative initiatives in the 111th Congress, none of which received consideration, focused on two approaches toward Cuba's offshore oil development. The first approach would have allowed for U.S. investment in Cuba's offshore energy development, while the second approach would have imposed sanctions on individuals and foreign companies that helped the development of Cuba's offshore petroleum resources.

In the 112th Congress, the two legislative initiatives introduced to date also take contrasting approaches to Cuba's offshore oil development, but would not include U.S. investment in Cuba's offshore energy development. The first approach would allow for the sanctioning of companies involved in Cuba's offshore oil development if the companies also wanted to conduct hydrocarbon operations in U.S. offshore waters. The second approach would impose requirements on companies conducting hydrocarbon operations off the coast of Cuba if the companies also wanted leases for oil and gas development in U.S. waters, and would also require the development and implementation of oil spill response plans for nondomestic oil spills in the Gulf of Mexico, including a joint contingency plan with Mexico, Cuba, and the Bahamas.

111th Congress

In the 111th Congress, legislative initiatives reflected two contrasting policy approaches toward Cuba's development of its offshore oil reserves. One approach would have allowed for U.S. involvement in Cuba's offshore oil sector, while the other approach would have imposed sanctions on foreign companies and individuals who assisted the development of Cuba's petroleum resources.

Reflecting the first approach, S. 774 (Dorgan), H.R. 1918 (Flake), and S. 1517 (Murkowski) would have authorized U.S. companies to work with Cuba for the exploration and extraction of oil, and to export without license all necessary equipment to Cuba. The bills would have amended the Trade Sanctions Reform and Export Enhancement Act of 2000 or TSRA (P.L. 106-387, Title IX) to provide for a general license for travel by persons engaging in hydrocarbon exploration and extraction activities. H.R. 1918 would have gone further and allowed for the importation of hydrocarbon resources from Cuba. In addition to these initiatives that specifically would have authorized involvement in Cuba's offshore energy sector, several other broader legislative initiatives in the 111th Congress that would have lifted all economic sanctions on Cuba by default would have allowed for U.S. investment in Cuba's energy sector.

In contrast, reflecting the second approach, H.R. 5620 (Ros-Lehtinen), the Caribbean Coral Reef Protection Act of 2010, would have imposed visa restrictions and economic sanctions on foreign nationals who helped facilitate the development of Cuba's petroleum resources. The initiative would have amended the Cuban Liberty and Democratic Solidarity Act of 1996 (P.L. 104-114) to exclude from the United States certain aliens (and their spouses, minor children, or agents) whose companies invested $1 million or more that contributed to the ability of Cuba to develop its offshore petroleum resources. The bill also would have provided for the imposition of sanctions if the President determined that a person had made an investment on or after January 10, 2005 of $1 million or more (or any combination of investments that equaled or exceeded $1 million or more in any 12-month period) that contributed to the enhancement of the Cuba's ability to develop its offshore petroleum resources. If such a determination were made, the President would have been required to propose two or more sanctions from a menu of sanctions listed in the bill.

112th Congress

Interest in Cuba's offshore oil development continues in the 112th Congress, with interest focused on a potential oil spill. To date, two legislative initiatives have been introduced that take different approaches, and

Representative Ros-Lehtinen has indicated that she will reintroduce the "Caribbean Coral Reef Protection Act" that had been introduced in the 111th Congress (see above.)[79]

H.R. 372 (Buchanan), introduced January 26, 2011, would amend the Outer Continental Shelf Lands Act to authorize the Secretary of the Interior to deny oil and gas leases and permits "to persons who engage in activities with the government of any foreign country that is subject to any sanction or an embargo" by the U.S. government. The intent of the legislation is to provide a disincentive to companies involved, or contemplating becoming involved, in Cuba's oil development, although the scope of the legislation is much broader and could affect other oil companies, including U.S. companies, not involved in Cuba. Because the bill does not define "sanction," the term could be used to refer to such U.S. restrictions as export controls or limits on foreign assistance. With this use of the term, many countries worldwide could be construed as being subject to a U.S. sanction, and as a result, any energy company that engages in activities with one of these countries could be denied an oil and gas lease in the United States under the proposed legislation.

S. 405 (Nelson), introduced February 17, 2011, would require a company that is conducting oil or gas operations off the coasts of Cuba to submit an oil response plan for their Cuba operations and demonstrate sufficient resources to respond to a worst case scenario if the company wanted to lease drilling rights in the United States. The bill would also require the Secretary of the Interior to carry out an oil spill risk analysis and planning process for the development and implementation of oil spill response plans for nondomestic oil spills in the Gulf of Mexico. The Secretary of the Interior would be required, among other things, to include recommendations for Congress on a joint contingency plan with the countries of Mexico, Cuba, and the Bahamas to ensure an adequate response to oil spills located in the eastern Gulf of Mexico.

CONCLUSION

Concern over Cuba's offshore oil development is likely to continue, especially if exploratory drilling begins as anticipated in 2011. An oil spill in Cuban waters potentially could carry oil to U.S. waters and coastal areas in Florida, and potentially could threaten marine and coastal resources. While the U.S. government has licensed some companies to provide oil spill prevention and containment support to companies operating in Cuba in the event of a large spill, policymakers may want to review whether U.S.-Cuban government engagement is warranted in order to maximize preparedness and response in the event of a major spill. Legislative initiatives already have been introduced in the 112th Congress reflecting contrasting approaches toward Cuba's offshore development.

End Notes

[1] Unless otherwise noted, data on oil volumes in this report come from the Energy Information Administration's *International Energy Statistics,* see http://tonto.eia.doe.gov/cfapps/ipdbproject/IEDIndex3.cfm.

[2] Christopher J. Schenk et al., *Assessment of Undiscovered Oil and Gas Resources of the North Cuba Basin, Cuba, 2004,* U.S. Department of the Interior, U.S. Geological Survey, World Assessment of Oil and Gas Fact Sheet, February 2005. http://walrus.wr.usgs.gov/infobank/programs/html/factsheets/pdfs/2005_3009.pdf.

[3] For an explanation of reserves and resources terms and concepts, please see CRS Report R40872, *U.S. Fossil Fuel Resources: Terminology, Reporting, and Summary,* by Gene Whitney, Carl E. Behrens, and Carol Glover

[4] Leslie Moore Mira, "Cuba lowers its resource estimate to 9 billion barrels: official," *Platts Commodity News,* April 5, 2011.

[5] Energy Information Administration (EIA), "Country Analysis Brief: Caribbean," U.S. Department of Energy. November 2009, http://www.eia.doe.gov/emeu/cabs/Caribbean/OilProduction.html.

[6] Bureau of Western Hemisphere Affairs, "Background Notes: Cuba," U.S. Department of State, March 25, 2010.

[7] Imports data is for 2007, the most recent available figures from EIA.

[8] "CNPC Secures Cuban oil contract," *China Economic Review,* November 24, 2010.

[9] "Exploration and Production: Operations," Repsol YPF, 2005 (accessed 11/8/2010), http://www.repsol.com/es_en/corporacion/accionistas-e-inversores/inf_economicofinanciera/informes_financieros/HTML/AreasNegocio/04/default.aspx?Pagina=16.

[10] Repsol, "Global Presence: Cuba," Repsol, April 30, 2010. http://www.repsol.com/es_en/corporacion/conocer-repsol/ presencia-global/cuba.aspx.

[11] Statoil is also looking to explore for oil in the Bahamas, where it has partnered with the Bahamas Petroleum Company. However, following the Deepwater Horizon oil spill, the Bahamian government suspended the consideration process for all oil exploration and drilling applications until the country has stringent environmental protocols in place to mitigate against a catastrophic oil well leak.

[12] Saipem is a subsidiary of publicly traded Italian oil major ENI S.p.a.

[13] Daniel Wallis, "Cuban oil rig set to cause waves in Washington," *Reuters,* May 17, 2011.

[14] "CIMC Raffles Delivers Scarabeo 9 to Saipem," *Rigzone,* October 7, 2010.

[15] Jeff Franks, "Arrival of Cuba offshore oil rig delayed again," *Reuters,* February 22, 2011.

[16] Daniel Wallis, "Cuban oil rig set to cause waves in Washington," *Reuters,* May 17, 2011.

[17] Jeff Franks, "Repsol moving ahead with Cuba oil plans," *Reuters,* April 5, 2011.

[18] Carlos Batista, "Cuba to drill five new oil wells by 2013," *AFP,* April 5, 2011.

[19] Note that Brazil's national oil company, Petrobras, has subsequently withdrawn from its offshore lease. Kate Joynes-Burgess, "Russia Comes to Cuba's Aid with Economic Deal," *IHS Global Insight Daily Analysis,* July 20, 2009. Bert Wilkinson, "Caribbean: China Consolidates Influence as U.S. Frets," *Inter Press News Service,* May 28, 2009. Daniel McCleary, "Brazil to Loan $300M to Cuba to Refurbish Port of Mariel," *Dow Jones International,* July 13, 2009.

[20] ONGC Videsh Limited, "Tender for Supply of Sub-sea Well Heads and Large OD Casting Pipes for Block-N34 and N-35 of Cuba Off-shore," press release, February 8, 2010, http://www.ongcvidesh.com/TenderFiles/31.pdf.

[21] "Gazprom Neft Heads for Cuba," *International Oil Daily, Energy Intelligence Group*, October 6, 2010.

[22] Gazprom has taken a 30% stake in the blocks originally contracted just to Petronas in a 2007 agreement with the Cuban government. "Gazprom Takes State In Cuban Offshore Blocks," *Rigzone*, November 16, 2010.

[23] PetroVietnam, "E&P Worldwide – Caribbean & South America," PetroVietnam, accessed Nov 11, 2010. *http://pvep.com.vn/Default.aspx?pageid=122&action=view&flash=cuba*.

[24] "Sonangol Signs Deal With Cuban Oil Company," *Angola Press Agency*, December 20, 2010.

[25] Rosa Tania Valdes, "Lula, Fidel Castro hold 'emotional' meeting," *Reuters*, February 24, 2010.

[26] Marc Frank, "Petrobras has relinquished Cuba oil block -official," *Reuters*, March 10, 2011.

[27] Jorge Piñon, *Cuba's Energy Crisis: Part III*, Cuba Transition Project, part of the Institute for Cuban and Cuban-American Studies at University of Miami, January 26, 2006, http://ctp.iccas.miami.edu/FOCUS_Web/Issue72.htm.

[28] See 15 CFR 734.4, which sets forth the 10% de minimis U.S. content provision in the Export Administration Regulations.

[29] This section is uses research and analysis from CRS Specialists Peter Folger, Jonathon Ramsuer, and Harold Upton.

[30] For background on the Deepwater Horizon Spill itself, see CRS Report R41262, *Deepwater Horizon Oil Spill: Selected Issues for Congress*, coordinated by Curry L. Hagerty and Jonathan L. Ramseur.

[31] In July 2010, the Secretary of the Interior changed the name of the Minerals Management Service (MMS) to Bureau of Oceans Energy Management, Regulation, and Enforcement (see Order No. 3302). MMS/BOEMRE's responsibilities are outlined in 30 C.F.R. § 250.

[32] "Significant Discoveries Marked '04," *Explorer* (Magazine of the American Society of Petroleum Geologists), January 2005.

[33] The International Maritime Organization (IMO) sent a technical assistance mission to Cuba in June 2010 to evaluate the level of preparation to respond to the Deepwater Horizon oil spill. The mission made several recommendations for Cuba to improve its national contingency plan, including the development of a training plan. See IMO, "Cuba, Misión de Asesoría Técnica," June 5-13, 2010, prepared by Klaus Essig.

[34] The Department of Interior defines a "loss of well control" as "uncontrolled flow of formation or other fluids, including flow to an exposed formation (an underground blowout) or at the surface (a surface blowout), flow through a diverter, or uncontrolled flow resulting from a failure of surface equipment or procedures". Also see Dagmar Schmidt Etkin, "Analysis of U.S. Oil Spillage," American Petroleum Institute, August, 2009. http://www.api.org/ehs/water/ spills/upload/356-Final.pdf.

[35] Construction of the rig was originally ordered by Norwegian firm Frigstad, but the contract was later transferred to Saipem. See more details on Scarabeo 9's specification at Saipem's website, available at http://www.snamprogetti.it/ media_gallery/brochure/Scarabeo9.pdf.

[36] Repsol, "Corporate Responsibility 2009," Repsol, April 26, 2010. http://www.repsol.com/ es_en/corporacion responsabilidad-corporativa/informe-responsabilidad-corporativa/ default.aspx. Note that Repsol, along with U.S. firm Pride of North America, is currently under investigation by a Spanish court for an offshore oil spill in the Mediterranean. Repsol officials have described the spill as "a minor one-time incident which was solved and cleaned up within days." (Martin Robert, "Spain court probes Repsol oil spillage: report," Reuters, July 2, 2010.)

[37] Desiree Connor, "Cuba says safety a priority in offshore oil plan," *Reuters*, May 12, 2011.

[38] Waters in the Florida Straits between Cuba and Florida move eastward from the Gulf of Mexico into the Atlantic Ocean, feeding the Gulf Stream. This is the Florida Current, which

stretches east and north through the Florida Straits and up the western side of the North Atlantic.

[39] International Tanker Owners Pollution Federation Limited (ITOPF), *Fate of Marine Oil Spills*, Technical Information Paper No.2, United Kingdom, 2002, http://www.itopf.com/_assets/documents/tip2.pdf.

[40] Ibid. Refined petroleum products, such as kerosene and gasoline, might evaporate completely. Heavier oils, or the heavier components of crude oil, may not undergo much evaporation; however, they may clump together and sink.

[41] Ibid.

[42] National Research Council (NRC), *Oil in the Sea III: Inputs, Fates, and Effects*, National Academies of Science, p. 4.

[43] Ibid., p. 127. These "sub-lethal" effects can occur at concentrations that are several orders of magnitude lower than concentrations that cause death.

[44] Ibid., p. 120.

[45] Ibid., p. 134. However, due to the increasing complexity of factors over time, studies on chronic effects are often met with debate and some controversy.

[46] These are 2008 figures provided by 'Visit Florida,' the state's official tourism marketing corporation. http://media.visitflorida.org/research.php.

[47] Lesley Clark, "U.S. Wary of Cuba's Drilling Plans, The Chief of the Miami Coast Guard Office Says His Agency Is Reviewing Response Scenarios for a Possible Spill Out of Cuba," *Miami Herald*, October 1, 2010; William Gibson, "Coast Guard Braces for Potential Cuban Oil Spill," *South Florida Sun-Sentinel*, March 23, 2011.

[48] For example, see *As Cuba Plans to Drill in the Gulf of Mexico, U.S. Policy Poses Needless Risks to Our National Interest*, Center for Democracy in the Americas, February 2011, available at http://democracyinamericas.org/pdfs/Cuba_Drilling_and_US_Policy.pdf.

[49] Jorge R. Piñon and Robert L. Muse, "Coping with the Next Oil Spill: Why U.S.-Cuba Environmental Cooperation is Critical," *U.S. Cuba Relations at Brookings*, Issue Brief No. 2, May 2010.

[50] Clifford Krauss, "Cuba's Oil Plans for Deep Waters Raise Concerns," *New York Times*, September 30, 2010.

[51] "U.S. Embargo May Hinder Oil Spill Response in Cuba Waters: Driller," *Platts Commodity News*, May 1, 2011.

[52] U.S. Department of State, "Cuba: Oil Exploration, Question at the July 16, 2010 Daily Press Briefing," July 19, 2010. OFAC licenses cover travel and any financial transactions while BIS licenses cover the export of commodities.

[53] Telephone conversation with Paul A. Schuler, President, Clean Caribbean & Americas (CCA), November 3, 2010. For further background on the work of CCA in Latin America and the Caribbean, see its website at http://www.cleancaribbean.org/cgi-bin/loadAll.cgi?toget=2index.

[54] For an explanation of the tiered oil spill response categories, see International Petroleum Industry Environmental Conservation Association (IPIECA), "Guide to Tiered Preparedness and Response," IPIECA Report Series Vol. 14, 2007.

[55] Telephone conversation with Paul A. Schuler, November 3, 2010. Also see "Florida Firm Ready to Clean Up in Event of Cuba Oil Spill," *CubaNews*, December 2010, pp. 14-15.

[56] Monica Hatcher, "Cuba Drilling Poses Spill Issue Group Says Trade Embargo Could Hinder a Response by the U.S.," *Houston Chronicle*, September 5, 2010. For further background on IADC, see http://www.iadc.org/.

[57] "U.S. Gives Permission for Cubans to Attend Drilling Conference," *Platts Commodity News*, April 28, 2011; See the agenda of the IADC conference, available at http://www.iadc.org/conferences/Environment_2011/.

[58] U.S. Department of State, "Mexico, Pollution: Marine Environment, Agreement signed at Mexico City, July 24, 1980," TIAS, 10021.

[59] United States Coast Guard, "Mexus Plan, The Joint Contingency Plan Between the United Mexican States and the United States of America Regarding Pollution of the Marine Environment by Discharges of Hydrocarbons and Other Hazardous Substance," February 25, 2000.

[60] For background on U.S. cooperation with Cuba on migration and drug trafficking, see CRS Report R41617, *Cuba: Issues for the 112th Congress*.

[61] National Commission on the BP Deepwater Horizon Oil Spill and Offshore Drilling, *Deepwater, The Gulf Oil Disaster and the Future of Offshore Drilling*, Report to the President, p. 254 and p. 300. See the full text of the report at http://www.oilspillcommission.gov/sites/default/files/documents/DEEPWATER_ReporttothePresident_FINAL.pdf

[62] Tom Doggett, "U.S. fears Cuba oil drilling, Mexico suggests talks," April 20, 2011.

[63] Jorge R. Piñon, "Joint Spill Planning," *Oil & Gas Journal*, March 7, 2011.

[64] U.S. Congress, Senate, "International Convention on Oil Pollution Preparedness, Response, and Co-operation, 1990," 102d Congress, 1st Session, Treaty Doc. 102-11, August 1, 1991 (Washington: GPO).

[65] U.S. Department of State, "Marine Pollution, Wider Caribbean Region, Convention between the United States of America and Other Governments, Cartagena, March 14, 1983," TIAS 11085.

[66] See the website of the IMO's regional Caribbean center at http://cep.unep.org/racrempeitc.

[67] IMO, "Cuba, Misión de Asesoría Técnica," June 5-13, 2010, prepared by Klaus Essig, pp. 41-42.

[68] For background, see U.S. Government Accountability Office, U.S. Embargo on Cuba" Recent Regulatory Changes and Potential Presidential or Congressional Actions," September 17, 2009; and Dianne E. Rennack and Mark P. Sullivan, *U.S.-Cuban Relations: An Analytic Compendium of U.S. Policies, Laws, & Regulations*, The Atlantic Council, Washington, DC, March 2005.

[69] Jake Colvin, "The Case for Business," in *9 Ways for US to Talk to Cuba & For Cuba to Talk to US*, The Center for Democracy in the Americas, Washington, DC, 2009.

[70] "Cuba: A New Policy of Critical and Constructive Engagement, Report of the Brookings Project on U.S. Policy Toward a Cuba in Transition," Brookings Institution, April 2009.

[71] Frank Calzón, "Search for Oil Won't Cure the Economy," *Miami Herald*, October 1, 2010.

[72] U.S. Department of State, Bureau of Oceans and International Environmental and Scientific Affairs, "Limits in the Seas, No. 110, Maritime Boundary: Cuba – United States," February 21, 1990.

[73] U.S. Congress, Senate Committee on Foreign Relations, *Three Treaties Establishing Maritime Boundaries Between the United States and Mexico, Venezuela, and Cuba*, (to accompany Execs. F, G & H, 96-1), 96th Cong., 2nd sess., August 5, 1980, Executive Rept. No. 96-49, p. 19.

[74] Ibid., p. 26. Also for a discussion of the provisional application of treaties, see U.S. Congress, Senate Committee on Foreign Relations, *Treaties and Other International Agreements: The Role of the United States Senate*, committee print, prepared by the Congressional Research Service, 106th Cong., 2nd sess., January 2001, S. Prt. 106-71 (Washington: GPO, 2001), pp. 113-114.

[75] Lesley Clark and Sara Kennedy, "Cuba Ready to Drill for Oil Deeper Than BP," *Miami Herald*, September 30, 2010.

[76] Jorge R. Piñon and Jonathan Benjamin-Alvarado, "Extracting Cuba's Oil and Gas: Challenges and Opportunities," in *Cuba's Energy Future*, ed. by Jonathan Benjamin-Alvarado, Brookings Institution Press, Washington, DC, 2010. p. 31.

[77] The Senate Committee on Foreign Relations reported the treaty favorably in September 2000, and the full Senate agreed to the resolution of advice and consent to ratification on October 18, 2000. See U.S. Senate, *Treaty with Mexico on Delimitation of Continental Shelf*, 106th Congress, 2nd sess., July 27, 2000, Treaty Doc. 106-39; and U.S. Congress, Senate

Committee on Foreign Relations, *Treaty with Mexico on Delimitation of the Continental Shelf,* 106th Cong., 2nd sess., September 29, 2000, Exec. Rept. 106-19.

[78] The role of the CLCS is to facilitate the implementation of the U.N Convention on the Law of the Sea with regard to the establishment of the outer limits of the continental shelf beyond 200 nautical miles. The Commission considers data and other material submitted by coastal states concerning the outer limits of the continental shelf and makes recommendations to coastal states on such matters, but without prejudice to the question of delimitation of the continental shelf between states with opposite or adjacent coasts. See the homepage of the CLCS, available at http://www.un.org/Depts/los/clcs_new/clcs_home.htm.

[79] "Ros-Lehtinen to be Briefed by Coast Guard on Cuba's Proposed Oil Exploration; Ileana Will Reintroduce Legislation to Discourage the Development of Cuba's Oil Drilling," Office of Congresswoman Ileana Ros-Lehtinen, Press Release, March 18, 2011.

In: Offshore Oil and Gas Resources in the U.S. ...   ISBN: 978-1-62100-256-7
Editor: Ethan L. Conrad   © 2012 Nova Science Publishers, Inc.

Chapter 3

ISRAEL'S OFFSHORE NATURAL GAS DISCOVERIES ENHANCE ITS ECONOMIC AND ENERGY OUTLOOK

Michael Ratner

SUMMARY

Israel has been dependent on energy imports since it became a nation in 1948, but the recent offshore natural gas discoveries could change that and possibly make Israel an exporter of natural gas. Development of the recently discovered natural gas fields—Tamar, Dalit, and Leviathan—likely will decrease Israel's needs for imported natural gas, imported coal, and possibly imported oil. A switch to natural gas would most likely affect electric generation, but could also improve Israel's trade balance and lessen carbon dioxide emissions. Regionally, Israel's success thus far has sparked interest from its neighbors to explore their boundaries for energy resources and has raised concerns from Lebanon about sovereignty over the discoveries. Development of these new resources, and possibly other discoveries, would enhance Israel's economic and energy security. Israel is in the early stages of formulating the regulatory framework to oversee the development of these resources and may seek assistance from the United States or other natural gas producing countries in weighing its options.

Key Points:

- The new discoveries—depending upon the actual production—could represent over 200 years' worth of Israel's current natural gas consumption.
- Israel's electrical generation sector will likely be the beneficiary of the new natural gas resources.
- Additional natural gas and possibly oil resources may exist.

INTRODUCTION

Israel's energy sector is set to undergo significant changes that could transform the country into an exporter of natural gas. Development of three recently discovered natural gas fields—Tamar, Dalit, and Leviathan (see **Figure 1**)—is projected to begin at the end of 2012 and be completed by the end of the decade. The estimated supplies from these fields (see **Table 1**) would enable Israel to decrease its natural gas and coal imports and possibly its oil imports.

Table 1. Israel's Estimated New Natural Gas Resources.

Field	Resource (trillion cubic feet)	Expected Production Date
Tamar	8.4	2012-2013
Dalit	0.5	2013-2014
Leviathan	16.0	2016-2018

Source: Noble Energy.

Note: Resources or resource base is a broad term that includes reserves (see below) as well as natural gas less likely to be produced. Resources are not subject to today's technology or price constraints as reserves are and may be produced sometime in the future. Reserve is an industry term to define the likelihood that natural gas resources can be produced using current technology and at today's prices according to the Society of Petroleum Engineers and the World Petroleum Congresses definition.

Coal imports would likely be most affected as coal is currently the primary fuel for electric generation, and can be displaced by natural gas. Israel's trade balance would likely improve and its carbon dioxide emissions would likely decline as a result. The discovery of natural gas resources has also led Israel to reevaluate the nation's energy tax policy. Israel's Ministry of Finance has recommended tax policy changes that would increase tax revenues, but decrease potential after-tax profits for developers. Regionally, Israel's success thus far has sparked interest from its neighbors to explore their boundaries for energy resources and has raised concerns from Lebanon about sovereignty over the discoveries.

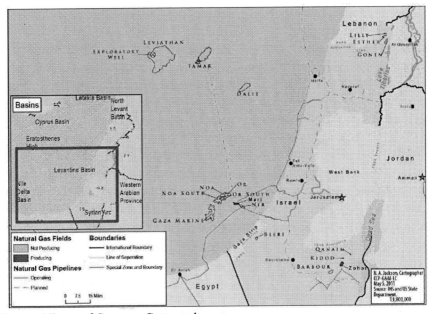

Source: Library of Congress Cartography.
Note: Inset depicts the regional geologic basins and the red box highlights where the new discoveries are in the Levantine Basin.

Figure 1. Israel's Growing Natural Gas Sector.

NATURAL GAS DISCOVERIES IMPROVE ENERGY SECURITY

Israel is poised to became an energy producer and perhaps even a natural gas exporter provided its recent discoveries come to fruition. At the end of last year, Noble Energy, a U.S. independent energy company, reconfirmed its estimates for its third and largest natural gas discovery off the northern coast of Israel. The Leviathan field has an estimated resource base of 16 trillion cubic feet (tcf)[1] of natural gas, but will require at least two more appraisal wells to be drilled before the size of the resource base is better defined.[2] Noble Energy's other natural gas discoveries (Tamar and Dalit) coupled with the success of other companies puts Israel in a position to be self sufficient in natural gas and possibly become a natural gas exporter, thus improving the country's energy and economic security.

Since January 2009, Noble Energy has made three natural gas discoveries—Tamar, Dalit, and Leviathan—with an estimated 25 tcf of resources. Israel's natural gas reserves—natural gas that has been discovered and can be expected to be economically produced—prior to the Noble Energy discoveries were estimated at 1.5 tcf or about 16 years worth at current production levels. If only half the natural gas from the new discoveries is produced at today's production levels, Israel would have well over a 100-year supply of natural gas. It is too early to know the rate of natural gas recovery from the three new fields or if other discoveries will arise, but it is highly likely that Israel's energy mix will move towards natural gas by the end of the decade. Tamar's first production is expected at the end of 2012, with Dalit one or two years after that, and Leviathan between 2016 and 2018.[3] According to Noble Energy, Tamar alone is expected to reach a maximum capacity of one billion cubic feet per day (bcf/d) by 2013 or 2014, or over three times the rate of Israeli consumption in 2009 of 0.31 bcf/d.[4]

Until 2008, Israel's demand for natural gas was met by domestic production. An import pipeline from Egypt began deliveries in 2008 and despite public discontent against the sales in Egypt, the pipeline remains operational today (**Figure 2** illustrates Israel's natural gas consumption and highlights the effect of Egyptian imports). Natural gas from the new fields could displace the Egyptian imports, which has benefits and disadvantages for both countries. Israel pays below market prices for the natural gas it imports from Egypt. Continuing the imports and using additional production to begin exports, most likely to Europe or Jordan, could further improve Israel's energy and economic security. Eliminating the imports could improve Israel's trade balance and provide greater supply security. For Egypt, stopping the exports to Israel would have political advantages as the natural gas sales to Israel were unpopular with Egyptians and were taken into court. The impact of the current unrest in Egypt on its natural gas exports to Israel is unclear. Maintaining the exports to Israel could help Egypt's trade balance.

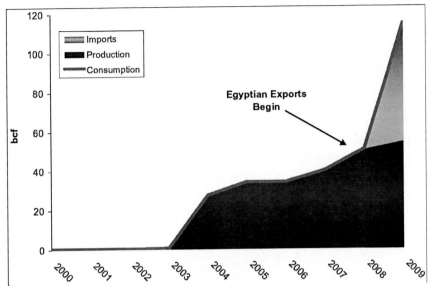

Source: Cedigaz databases, http://www.cedigaz.org.
Notes: Production plus imports less exports equals consumption. Israel has never been an exporter of natural gas.

Figure 2. Israeli Natural Gas Consumption and Sources.
Units = billion cubic feet (bcf).

Egyptian Unrest

At the end of April, the natural gas terminal near El-Arish in Egypt (see **Figure 1** above) was attacked for the second time since protests erupted in that country in January.[5] Natural gas from the terminal supplies the Arab Gas Pipeline to Jordan, Syria, and Lebanon, and a separate pipeline to Israel. There is no estimate for how long natural gas will not be exported. The pipeline was also attacked and disabled in February causing natural gas supplies to be stopped for about a month. The terminal has been a target for Bedouins who feel neglected and oppressed by Cairo.[6]

Minimal Use of Natural Gas Currently

Israel's consumption of natural gas has been growing since 2003, but remains a relatively small portion of its current energy mix at 11%.[7] Oil accounts for almost half of Israel's primary energy consumption, while coal is 35%. (See **Figure 3.**) However, the recent natural gas discoveries have the potential to substantially change the share of natural gas use in Israel. Industry forecasts project that by 2015, Israel could be consuming 1 bcf of natural gas per day, an almost threefold increase from today's consumption.[8] The three new natural gas fields represent potentially 26 times the total amount of energy currently consumed annually by Israel from all fuel sources. Israel's electricity generation sector will most likely utilize the new resources more than other sectors (see section below) and could even facilitate Israel moving towards electrification of its car fleet, a goal the government has set. Current energy infrastructure is equipped primarily for oil and coal; substituting natural gas would require major changes and investment to the electricity and transportation sectors.

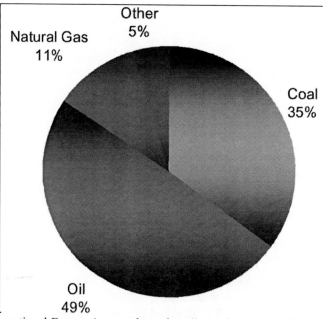

Source: International Energy Agency data—http://www.iea.org/stats/balancetable.asp?
    COUNTRY_CODE=IL.
Notes: A conversion factor of 7.33 was used to go from metric tones of oil equivalent
    to barrels of oil equivalent.

Figure 3. Israeli Primary Energy Consumption by Fuel. 2008 total was 22 million metric tonnes of oil equivalent or 161 million barrels of oil equivalent.

Electricity Generation Sector Likely to be Transformed

Israel's electricity generation sector will most likely undergo the greatest change because of the development of Israel's natural gas resources. Currently, natural gas fuels about 26% of Israel's electric generation. (See **Figure 4**.) Coal supplies almost two-thirds of the generation capacity. If Israel were to convert all of its existing electric power generation to natural gas, it would require approximately an additional 0.8 bcf/d of natural gas,[9] the estimated maximum output from the Tamar natural gas field alone. Replacing only its coal units would require approximately 0.67 bcf/d of natural gas. If these conversions were to occur, carbon dioxide emissions from the electricity generation sector would decrease 52% and 50%, respectively.[10] However, this would be a major investment and likely require many years to achieve.

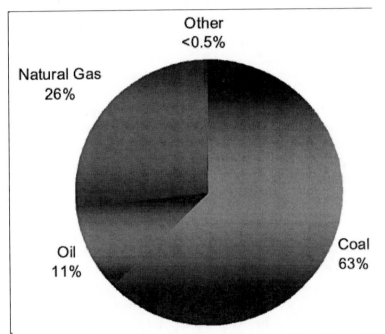

Source: International Energy Agency data—http://www.iea.org/stats/balancetable.asp? COUNTRY_CODE=IL.

Notes: Other includes hydroelectric power, wind, and various other sources.

Figure 4. Israeli Electricity Fuel Mix. 2008 total was 56,420 gigawatt hours.

Switching to a natural gas-based electrical sector would allow Israel to increase the domestic share of energy production. Currently, Israel imports all of its coal and most of its oil.

RELATED ISSUES

Proposed Energy Tax Changes[11]

In April 2010, Israel's Minister of Finance appointed a committee to examine fiscal policy related to oil and gas resources in Israel, prompted by the recent natural gas discoveries.[12] The committee was directed by Israel's Minister of Finance to (1) evaluate Israel's fiscal system as it relates to oil and gas reserves and compare Israel's system to countries in similar economic circumstances; (2) propose an updated fiscal system; and (3) examine the potential effects current and future natural gas discoveries would have on the Israeli economy.[13]

The committee's draft conclusions were released by Finance Ministry on November 10, 2010.[14] The committee found that "the current system does not properly reflect the public's ownership of its natural resources."[15] The committee's draft conclusions recommended two major changes to Israel's tax treatment of the oil and gas industry. First, the draft conclusions suggested eliminating the existing depletion deduction.[16] Second, a progressive tax on oil and gas profits was proposed. In the proposal, profits were determined using the ratio of total revenues to total exploration and development costs. The committee's draft conclusions did not recommend a change in Israel's royalty rate, which is set at 12.5%.[17]

The committee's final report was released on January 3, 2011, and fully accepted by Prime Minister Netanyahu and the cabinet.[18] Overall, the committee's recommendations would increase the government's share on oil and gas revenues to between 52% and 62%, up from the current 30%.[19] Like the draft conclusions, the committee's final recommendations suggest eliminating the depletion allowances and imposing a tax on oil and gas profits. The tax on profits would start after the project had earned cumulative net income equal to 150% of its exploration and development costs.[20] The rate of tax would start at 20%, increasing to maximum rate of 50%.[21]

This tax increase would be phased in over time. Fields that start production prior to 2014—which would likely include Tamar and possibly Dalit, but not Leviathan—would be partially exempt from the tax increase. For reserves in which extraction begins by January 1, 2014, the profits tax will not apply until cumulative net income reaches 200% of exploration and development costs and will not be fully phased in until reaching 280%.

The tax increase recommended in the final report was less than was initially presented in the draft proposal.[22] The proposed tax increases will be enacted only if approved by the Israeli government. Israeli and U.S. companies oppose any tax increase, and argue that changing the tax regime will deter future energy resource development.[23]

Comparison to U.S. Energy Tax Policy[24]

Oil and gas producers in the United States pay the U.S. corporate income tax. The corporate tax is levied on taxable income, which is calculated as gross income less deductions. The statutory corporate income tax rate is generally 35%. There are a number of deductions specific to the oil and gas industry, such as the ability to expense intangible drilling costs (IDCs) and to claim percentage depletion instead of cost depletion.[25] Oil and gas producers are also eligible for the Section 199 production activity deduction.[26]

The United States has generally not imposed a specific profits tax above and beyond the corporate income tax on the oil and gas industry. However, from 1980 through 1988, the United States levied a windfall profits tax (WPT) on the U.S. oil industry. In practice, the WPT was an excise tax.[27] The tax was determined according to the price of oil rather than on profits. The WPT was enacted to address increased oil industry profits following the decontrolling of oil prices.[28]

Lebanon Contests Discoveries

The announcements by Israel and Noble Energy of significant natural gas discoveries have prompted Lebanese leaders to raise concerns that the natural gas fields are at least partially in Lebanese waters and that Israel will "steal" Lebanon's resources if the Lebanese government does not act. Lebanon and Israel have never defined their maritime border as the two countries are still technically at war. The Lebanese government has appealed to the United Nations, particularly the UN Interim Force in Lebanon, to intervene in defining the maritime border, but the UN has declined thus far to delineate the maritime border.[29] Some trade press for the natural gas industry is depicting all the Noble Energy discoveries within Israeli borders.[30]

There has been rhetoric from both the Lebanese and Israeli governments about using all means necessary, including military action, to defend their national resources, according to regional press reports.[31]

PROSPECTS FOR THE FUTURE

Export Potential Possible

Whether Israel will become an exporter of natural gas is yet to be determined. If the resource estimates are correct, the new fields would give Israel the resources to become an exporter. A number of factors raise doubts about the viability of exports: Growing domestic demand—and potential new uses for gas, energy security issues, the expense of liquefying the natural gas for transport, an existing global glut of natural gas, and the politics of pipeline exports. Noble Energy is exploring the possibility of building a liquefaction facility, possibly in Cyprus to utilize any natural gas discovered there, for exports to Europe and Asia, but it is too early to determine the feasibility of such a project.

Other Regional Natural Gas Development Likely

Hoping to replicate Israel's success in finding new energy resources, Cyprus, Lebanon, and Syria have announced timetables for holding auctions for licenses to explore for oil and gas. Cyprus and Syria plan to hold their license auctions this year, while Lebanon has theirs scheduled for 2012.[32] It is unclear how the ongoing political deadlock might affect the Lebanese government's plans to move forward with its energy development.[33] In December 2010, Cyprus and Israel signed an agreement defining their sea border.

In March 2010, The U.S. Geological Survey (USGS) released a report on the Levant Basin province that stretches from the Sinai peninsula to the northern border of Syria and from the coast into the Mediterranean Sea to the western side of Cyprus. The report stated that the Levant Basin may hold 1.7 billion barrels of recoverable oil and 122 trillion cubic feet of recoverable natural gas.[34]

Oil Discoveries Possible

In light of the USGS report, Noble Energy and its partners have raised the prospect of drilling deeper, below the natural gas bearing formations in the Leviathan field in search of oil. Noble Energy estimates that there is a 17% probability that it could find 3 billion barrels of oil.[35] The probability and estimate will likely change as additional information and data is gathered.

POLICY CONSIDERATIONS

The U.S. government[36] is not directly involved in Israel's oil and gas policies. However, in the near-term, consultations regarding the energy policy and regulations would be one area that government to government interaction might take place. Israel has never been a major energy producer and must balance its normal economic and security concerns with development of this new resource. The United States has experience related to regulatory oversight, tax policy, and environmental concerns that could benefit Israel.

The regional interest from other countries to develop energy resources creates an opportunity for discussions between Israel and its neighbors, bilaterally or multilaterally and directly or indirectly. Additionally, resolving the maritime demarcation issue between Israel and Lebanon would alleviate industry uncertainty.

ACKNOWLEDGMENTS

Molly Sherlock, Analyst in Economics, contributed to this report.

End Notes

[1] The units used throughout this paper vary from billion cubic feet (bcf) to trillion cubic feet (tcf or 1,000 times 1 bcf) to bcf per day (bcf/d or 1 bcf divided by 365).
[2] *Noble Energy Announces Significant Discovery at Leviathan Offshore Israel*, Nobel Energy Press Release, December 29, 2010, http://www.nobleenergyinc.com.
[3] Conversation with Noble Energy, January 10, 2011.

[4] Cedigaz databases, an international industry association—http://www.cedigaz.org. See "Minimal Use of Natural Gas Currently" section below for background on current Israeli energy consumption.

[5] Ashraf Sweilam, Explosion rocks Egypt gas terminal near Israel, *Associated Press*, April 27, 2011.

[6] Ibid.

[7] International Energy Agency data—http://www.iea.org/stats/balancetable.asp?COUNTRY_CODE=IL.

[8] Conversation with Noble Energy about their estimates for the Israeli consumption of natural gas. Their estimate did not include converting Israel's coal-fired electric power to natural gas; January 10, 2011.

[9] This assumes utilizing high efficiency combined cycle gas turbines to generate the electricity. This type of power plant is common and considered an industry standard for new natural gas generation.

[10] Based on International Energy Agency production data and industry estimates for carbon dioxide emissions from electric power plants.

[11] Analysis of Israel's energy taxes and proposed changes was provided by Molly Sherlock of CRS.

[12] Israel's oil and gas tax policy had been left largely unchanged since the 1950s.

[13] State of Israel: Ministry of Finance, *Summary of the Draft Conclusions by the Committee to Examine the Policy on Oil and Gas Resources in Israel*, Headed by Prof. Eytan Sheshinski, November 10, 2010. Available at http://www.financeisrael.mof.gov.il/FinanceIsrael/Pages/En/News/20101110.aspx.

[14] The full committee report has not yet been released. CRS has relied on the English version of the Executive Summary of the committee's recommendation as well as secondary sources in the overview presented here. The English translation of the Executive Summary is available at http://www.financeisrael.mof.gov.il/FinanceIsrael/Docs/ En/publications/ 20110110_Sheshinski_Executive_Summary_of_Final_Conclusions_Eng.pdf. A Hebrew version of the final report is available from Israel's Ministry of Finance at http://www.mof.gov.il/BudgetSite/Reform/Pages/ PhysicsPolicy.aspx.

[15] State of Israel: Ministry of Finance, p. 3.

[16] Depletion deductions allow taxpayers to account for a reduction in a product's reserves. The deduction reduces taxable income, thereby reducing tax liability. The commission's draft conclusions provided a rationale for eliminating the depletion deduction. The commission noted that the depletion deduction was intended to compensate owners of mineral assets for the asset's reduced value following resource extraction. In the present case, the asset is owned by the state. Thus, allowing depletion deductions does not compensate the asset owner (the state) for a reduction in asset value.

[17] For comparison, royalty payments in the United States are generally between 12.5% and 30% of the gross wellhead value of production, depending on the lease contract.

[18] The recommendations still need to be passed by Israel's parliament before they take effect. See *Netanyahu "fully accepts" Sheshinski C'tee findings*, Jerusalem Post, January 18, 2011; Ethan Bronner, "Israel Approves Doubling of Taxes on Oil and Gas Extraction Profits," *New York Times*, January 23, 2011.

[19] Guy Chazan, "Israel Sets Steep Rise in Taxes on Oil, Gas," *The Wall Street Journal*, January 4, 2010.

[20] Net cumulative income is defined as cumulative income less project expenses, royalty payments, and profits taxes paid in previous years.

[21] The 50% rate would be applied once the ratio of net cumulative income to exploration and development costs reaches 230%.

[22] The draft proposal would have imposed a 60% to 70% tax on earnings above 150% of a company's investment.

[23] Vita Bekkar, *Delek warns of impact from Israeli tax regime*, Financial Times, January 4, 2011.

[24] Comparison to U.S. energy taxes was provided by Molly Sherlock of CRS.

[25] Cost depletion allows for the recovery of the actual capital investment. With cost depletion, total deductions cannot exceed the original capital investment. Under percentage depletion, the deduction for recovery of a capital investment is a percentage of the "gross income"—that is, revenue—from the sale of the mineral. With percentage depletion, total deductions may exceed the initial capital investment.

[26] Internal Revenue Code (IRC) § 199 allows domestic manufacturers to take a deduction from net income. Most manufacturers are allowed a deduction of 9%. Oil and gas producers are allowed a reduced deduction of 6%.

[27] Excise taxes are typically imposed on a transaction, rather than on a person or corporation. Excise taxes can be levied on a per-unit basis or ad valorem basis.

[28] For additional background, see CRS Report RL33305, *The Crude Oil Windfall Profit Tax of the 1980s: Implications for Current Energy Policy*, by Salvatore Lazzari.

[29] Neal Sandler, *UN rejects call to delineate the Lebanese-Israeli maritime border*, Platts, January 5, 2011.

[30] *Israeli gas heightens interest in Eastern Mediterranean*, Wood Mackenzie Consulting, November 2010, p. 2.

[31] *Shami Wants UN To Keep An Eye on Israel Oil Aims*, NOW Lebanon, January 4, 2011; *Israel's Discovery of Natural Gas Threatens Lebanon's Rights!*, Al-Manar, January 2, 2011.

[32] *Israeli gas heightens interest in Eastern Mediterranean*, Wood Mackenzie Consulting, November 2010, p. 5.

[33] For more information on Lebanon, see CRS Report R40054, *Lebanon: Background and U.S. Relations*, by Casey L. Addis.

[34] *Assessment of Undisclosed Oil and Gas Resources of the Levant Basin Province, Eastern Mediterranean*, USGS, March 2010.

[35] Avi Bar-Eli, *Leviathan Natural Gas Reserves Said Worth $90 Billion*, Haaretz, December 30, 2010.

[36] For more information on Israel/U.S. relations, see CRS Report RL33476, *Israel: Background and U.S. Relations*, by Jim Zanotti.

INDEX